Summary

The Lambeth Group underlies the London and Hampshire Basins. While of limited outcrop, it is of considerable relevance to infrastructure developments in central London, particularly those of tunnelling and deep foundations. Its complex stratigraphy has recently been clarified. This, in turn, has led to a better engineering description and classification. An improved understanding of the engineering behaviour and properties of its component units has been gained from several recent major projects in central London with high-quality ground investigations and laboratory testing.

This publication draws together this new information, coupling it with a review of case histories of construction in the Lambeth Group. There is less information on engineering properties of the Lambeth Group farther from London, but examples are given of the engineering performance of these materials at their outcrop. Guidance is given about the relation between engineering properties and the Group's widely differing lithologies, about the hazards they pose for construction, and appropriate ways to overcome them. Recommendations are given for investigating these complex materials. In addition to case study data, the report is supported by a comprehensive reference list and bibliography.

Acknowledgements

This report is one outcome of CIRIA Research Project 576 "The engineering properties of major UK soils and rocks: Mercia Mudstone Group, Lambeth Group."

Research contractor   **Maunsell Limited** carried out the overall research project under a contract with CIRIA. Dr D W Hight of the Geotechnical Consulting Group and Mr R A Ellison of the British Geological Survey, were commissioned directly by CIRIA for this work.

Authors   **Dr D W Hight** (Chapters 4, 6 and 7) is one of the founding directors of the Geotechnical Consulting Group and has been responsible for specialist advice to consulting firms, contractors, public authorities, solicitors and oil companies on various UK and overseas projects involving foundations, retaining walls, earthworks design, slope stability, site investigation and laboratory testing. Dr Hight has published widely on the subjects of soil behaviour, offshore geotechnics, soil sampling, stability problems and foundations and has delivered prestigious lectures at many venues worldwide including the Rankine Lecture in 1998.

Mr D Page (Chapters 3, 5 and associated appendices) of High-Point Rendel. It was on Darren's first-ever geological field trip that he examined the Lambeth Group at Newhaven. He went on to manage the geotechnical aspects of the Jubilee Line Extension Project for London Underground Ltd. The boreholes and excavations for the JLEP and investigations for the East London Line Extension and Crossrail formed the basis of his MSc thesis.

Mr R A Ellison (Chapter 2 and Appendix 2) is principal geologist at the British Geological Survey where he has worked for 30 years. He has been involved with work on the Lambeth Group since the 1980s when he looked at borehole cores in Essex, and later in south-east London for a proposed rail link from the Channel Tunnel. Subsequently he was responsible for the geological mapping of Greater London and acted as a consultant on the Lambeth Group, including the London Underground Jubilee Line Extension, proposed Crossrail route and Channel Tunnel Rail Link. This work led him to propose a subdivision of the Lambeth Group that has been adopted as the standard for London. He has published several papers and geological memoirs concerning Tertiary geology in the London Basin, most recently a Geology of London memoir to be published in 2004. He is currently regional geologist for south-west England.

The contribution of Mr R A Ellison is made with the permission of the director, British Geological Survey.

CIRIA managers   CIRIA's research managers were **Dr A J Pitchford** and **Mr F M Jardine**.

Steering group	Following CIRIA's usual practice the research was guided by a steering group, which comprised:	
Chairman	**Dr J D Lewis**	TRL Ltd
Members	Dr J P Apted	Hyder Consulting Limited
	Mr D F T Nash	University of Bristol
	Dr G Austin	Austin Geotech
	Mr M G Black	London Underground Limited
	Dr G B Card	Card Geotechnics Limited
	Mr N J Langdon	Card Geotechnics Limited
	Mr D T Shilston	WS Atkins Consultants Limited

Project funders The project was funded under the Partners in Technology programme of the Construction Directorate of the Department of the Environment, Transport and the Regions.

Additional project funding and support in kind was provided by:

CIRIA's Core Programme

British Geological Survey

Geotechnical Consulting Group

Mr D P Page.

CIRIA and the authors gratefully acknowledge the support of these funding organisations and the technical help and advice provided by the members of the steering group and the many individuals and organisations who were consulted. Contributions do not imply that individual funders necessarily endorse all views expressed in published outputs.

Contributors The authors have benefited from discussions and information provided by the following individuals and organisations:

James Apted	Hyder
Fiona Chow	Geotechnical Consulting Group (additional piling references)
Croydon Tramlink	
East Sussex County Council	
Highways Agency	
Nick Langdon	Card Geotechnics Limited
Mott MacDonald	
David Pascall	Arup
Jackie Skipper	Natural History Museum
Southern Water	
Tony Vaughan	Shoreham Port Authority
West Sussex County Council	

Figures Figures in Section 2 are reproduced with the permission of the director, British Geological Survey and are copyright of the Natural Environment Research Council (NERC).

Contents

FIGURES

TABLES

CASE STUDIES

Abbreviations

Bgl	below ground level
BGS	British Geological Survey
BRE	Building Research Establishment
CA	anisotropically consolidated (triaxial tests)
CI	isotropically consolidated (triaxial tests)
CIRIA	Construction Industry Research and Information Association
CIU	isotropically consolidated undrained (test)
CPT	cone penetration test
CPTU	piezocone test
CTRL	Channel Tunnel Rail Link
DLR	Docklands Light Railway
DSB	drained shear box (test)
EPBM	earth pressure balance (tunnelling) machine
GS	glauconitic sand
HF	Harwich Formation
JLE	Jubilee Line Extension
Lb	laminated beds
LC	London Clay
LG	Lambeth Group
LINK-CMR	LINK Construction Maintenance and Refurbishment programme
LMC	Lower Mottled Clay
LSC	Lower Shelly Clay
M OD	metres relative to Ordnance datum
NATM	New Austrian tunnelling method
SCL	sprayed concrete lining (tunnelling)
SPT	standard penetration test
TC	triaxial compression
TE	triaxial extension
TG	Terrace Gravel
TRL	Transport Research Laboratory
TSF	Thanet Sand Formation
U100	general purpose sample (10 mm dia. open drive tube sample)
UF	Upnor Formation
UMC	Upper Mottled Clays
UU	unconsolidated undrained (triaxial) test
WIT	Waterloo International Terminal
Xrail	Crossrail
YMCA	Young Men's Christian Association

Notation

C'	effective stress cohesion intercept
c_u	undrained shear strength
C_u	undrained shear strength (both symbols are used in this document)
C_v	coefficient of consolidation
D	depth below ground level
E	void ratio
E_0	initial void ratio
E_{sec}	secant Young's modulus
E_u	undrained Young's modulus
$E_{u0.1}$	undrained Young's modulus at 0.1% axial strain
$E_{u0.01}$	undrained Young's modulus at 0.01% axial strain
f_s	shaft friction
$F(z/D)$	depth factor in borehole plate tests
G	shear modulus
G_{vh}	dynamic shear modulus
G_{hv}	dynamic shear modulus
G_{hh}	dynamic shear modulus
I_L	liquidity index
I_p	plasticity index
K	coefficient of permeability
k_h	coefficient of permeability (horizontal flow)
k_v	coefficient of permeability (vertical flow)
K_0	coefficient of earth pressure at rest
m_v	coefficient of compressibility
N	SPT blow-count
P	load per unit area of plate
P'	effective stress
P'_I	initial effective stress
P'_0	*in-situ* mean effective stress
P_{ult}	ultimate load in plate load tests
q_c	cone resistance
T	time
V_{vh}	shear wave velocity
V_{hv}	shear wave velocity
V_{hh}	shear wave velocity
W_0	initial water content
w_p	plastic limit
w_L	liquid limit
δ	settlement/plate diameter
Δe	change in void ratio
Σ_{v0}	initial vertical total stress
Σ'	effective stress
Σ'_n	effective normal stress
E	strain
N	Poisson's ratio
M	Poisson's ratio
Φ'	angle of shearing resistance
Φ'_p	peak angle of shearing resistance
Φ'_r	residual angle of shearing resistance

1   Introduction

The Lambeth Group (formerly known as the Woolwich and Reading Beds) is a complex sequence of gravels, sands and clays of Tertiary (Palaeogene) age, which exhibit considerable lateral and vertical variation. They were deposited in one or more embayments on the western edge of a deep water marine basin centred on the present North Sea over a period of about two million years (56–55 million years before present). The strata underlies parts of south-east England and is encountered in sub-surface engineering works throughout Greater London. Surface outcrops occur in Kent, Essex and Suffolk and in the Hampshire Basin. These strata affect the construction industry mainly in operations such as foundations, excavations and tunnelling. The properties of the material vary between those of an engineering soil and those of a rock, depending on the lithology, post-depositional diagenetic affects (eg cementation) and state of weathering (where exposed).

An appreciation of the conditions under which the Lambeth Group was deposited and its subsequent geological history are of considerable assistance in understanding its geotechnical properties and behaviour in engineering situations.

1.1   BACKGROUND

The Lambeth Group underlies much of south-east England, particularly in the London and Hampshire Basins. As a result the material is frequently encountered in major construction projects, such as Jubilee Line Extension Project (JLEP). The lithological variation in the strata and the lack of surface exposure resulted in generally poor understanding of the nature of the deposit, its depositional history and how it had been altered by post-depositional diagenetic changes. Work undertaken by the British Geological Survey and others (helped by the availability of site investigation information for projects including the JLEP) has improved understanding of the environment in which the sediments were deposited. In turn this is allowing engineering parameters to be applied to the materials with more confidence.

CIRIA identified the Lambeth Group as one of the "economically important UK soils and rocks" for which engineering guidance was required. This report is one of a series that covers engineering in glacial tills (Trenter, 1999), Chalk (Lord *et al*, 2002) and the Mercia Mudstone Group (Chandler and Forster, 2000). All these engineering materials are economically important to construction; they are difficult to sample and to test; and understanding their engineering behaviour relies upon a sound appreciation of the geological processes that have affected them since their deposition.

1.2   SCOPE AND OBJECTIVES

The purpose of the research project was to establish, assess and make available up-to-date information about the engineering properties of the Lambeth Group in order to improve the investigation, design and construction of ground engineering works in these materials.

Other weak rocks are not specifically considered in this report. Although information presented here may be of value to those concerned with the geotechnical behaviour of other weak rocks, care must be taken before extending experience with Lambeth Group deposits to other materials, however similar they may appear to be.

A useful discussion of the engineering properties of weak rocks, together with aspects of pile design, some of which is of direct relevance to Lambeth Group deposits, is given by Gannon *et al* (1999).

This account is a review of the current knowledge on the geology of the Lambeth Group. It is written with the view that it will be the primary source of background information on the Lambeth Group. It is aimed at those involved in all stages of planning, execution and monitoring of engineering projects. This includes geologists, engineering geologists, civil engineers, and drilling and tunnelling contractors.

1.3 STRUCTURE OF THE REPORT

Chapter 2 presents the geological history of the Lambeth Group. This chapter is supported by Appendix 1, which lists relevant Geological Survey Memoirs. Chapters 3 to 6 review the geotechnical aspects and recommend good practice when testing and designing with the gravels, sands and clays of the Lambeth Group. The basic properties of these heterogeneous materials are outlined, and the important issues for understanding the geotechnics of the Lambeth Group are highlighted. Relevant case studies are included in Chapter 5.

A comprehensive reference list and summaries of major case history data for tunnels, shafts, deep excavations and piling are contained within the appendices at the end of the report.

2   Geology of the Lambeth Group

The term Lambeth Group has been in the public domain since 1994 and replaces the Woolwich and Reading Beds. The term was introduced in order to clarify the stratigraphy shown on British Geological Survey maps, initially in the London area.

There are two reasons why the Lambeth Group warrants a review of this kind. First, the strata within the group exhibit considerable lateral and vertical lithological variation. Historically this has presented considerable engineering difficulties. Second, the Lambeth Group is within 50 m of the surface beneath large tracts of London and therefore has, and continues to be, an important issue in many engineering projects.

In the following account the principal constituent lithological units of the Lambeth Group are defined. Their correlation and three-dimensional relationships are demonstrated in a series of cross-sections and maps.

2.1   REGIONAL SETTING

Following deposition of the Chalk across much of Europe, there was increased tectonic and volcanic activity related to the opening of the Atlantic Ocean in latest Cretaceous and early Tertiary time. It was accompanied by a global fall in sea level, resulting in a greater land area. A phase of folding associated with the building of the Alps in southern Europe began, and a period of uplift caused tilting and the removal of the youngest part of the Chalk in southern England.

The start of intermittent deposition of Tertiary sediments took place about 58 million years ago when a shallow sea extended from the deeper water of the North Sea Basin to cover the whole of south-east England. The Lambeth Group forms part of this sedimentary sequence, laid down in a relatively short interval, about 56 to 55 million years ago. Gentle folding of the Lambeth Group strata took place in Miocene time, some 20 million years ago, when the London and Hampshire Basins became the separated outcrops that are familiar on geological maps of the UK (Figure 2 1).

2.2   DEPOSITIONAL ENVIRONMENT

The Lambeth Group was laid down in one or more embayments on the western margin of a deep water marine basin centred on the present North Sea. The period of deposition was characterised by small but significant variations in sea level, caused partly by contemporary earth movements and partly because of global climate changes. They resulted in periodic migration of the depositional environments and were a major contributory factor in the complex lithological changes observed in the Lambeth Group. As the sea level fell the sediments became exposed, soils developed, and there was downcutting by channels draining the new land. In contrast, sea level rising relative to the land led to rapid inundation followed by a new phase of marine sedimentation.

In general terms, shallow marine sands dominate the Lambeth Group succession in the east. Inland, towards the west, was a brackish water lagoon probably partly protected from the sea by a barrier-beach and in which shell beds and interfingering sands, silts and clays were laid down. Still further inland was a broad alluvial plain that may have been periodically inundated. Clays and silts dominate this area and channels, now filled with sand, meandered across it. The arrangement of these various environments is shown in Figure 2.2.

a

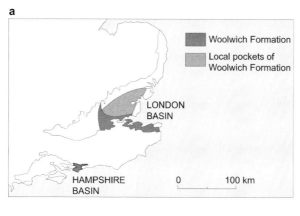

b

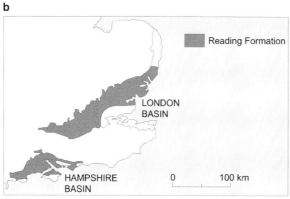

c

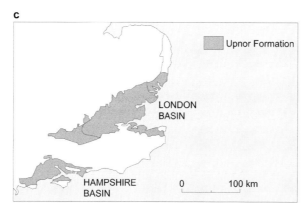

d

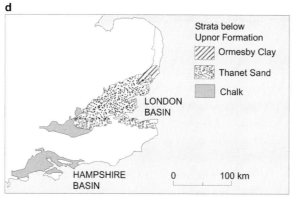

Figure 2.1   *Distribution of the Lambeth Group: (a) Woolwich Formation, (b) Reading Formation, (c) Upnor Formation, (d) underlying strata (© NERC)*

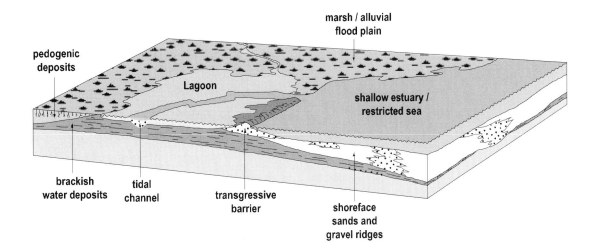

Figure 2.2 *The environment of deposition of the Lambeth Group (© NERC)*

2.3 HISTORICAL PERSPECTIVE

Exposures of deposits that constitute the Lambeth Group were first described in pioneering work by Prestwich (1854) and systematically mapped by the Geological Survey in the late nineteenth century. The findings of these surveys were published in Geological Survey Memoirs covering the London Basin (Whitaker, 1872) and much of the Hampshire Basin (Reid, 1898; 1902). Subsequently, memoirs covering the whole of the London and Hampshire Basins have been published. The most recent of these, in which there are accounts of the Lambeth Group, cover Southampton (Edwards and Freshney, 1987) and Bournemouth (Bristow *et al*, 1991) in the Hampshire Basin, and Chelmsford (Bristow, 1985) and Braintree (Ellison and Lake, 1986) in the London Basin.

Several distinct and well-known lithologies were identified in the Lambeth Group from the outset. Thus the deposits at the base of the Group in the London and Hampshire Basins were known as the Bottom Bed. These are now called the **Upnor Formation**, see Table 2.1. Above it, the Reading Beds (now called the **Reading Formation**) are predominant in the Hampshire Basin and in the north and west of the London Basin. In the extreme east of the Hampshire Basin and the south and east of the London Basin, deposits above the Bottom Bed were the Woolwich Beds (now called the **Woolwich Formation**). The distribution of these constituent formations is shown in Figure 2.1.

In an area coinciding more or less with central and south London, Hester (1965) identified a transition zone between what he termed the Reading type and Woolwich type strata where beds of intermediate type occur. It is principally in this zone where a new classification of the Lambeth Group has been achieved in recent years. Initially, the interpretation of borehole records, the results of drilling by BGS of cored boreholes, and detailed examination of exposures in Essex and Suffolk, led Ellison (1983) to recognise a relationship between several units of the Lambeth Group.

This work was developed further, and in more detail, in London as a result of the examination of numerous fully cored boreholes put down for major infrastructure projects. The main site investigations involved were for the proposed Channel Tunnel Rail Link (CTRL) route in south east London, the current CTRL route from Barking to Kings Cross, Crossrail and the Jubilee Line Extension. A combination of these borehole data and historical information on exposures and quarry sections has led to the establishment of informal lithological units in the London area.

Table 2.1 *Lambeth Group terminology*

Formation	Previous usage		Units with abbreviation used in this report	
	London Basin	Hampshire Basin		
Reading Formation	Reading Beds	Reading Beds	Upper Mottled Clay	UMC
			Lower Mottled Clay	LMC
			ferruginous sand*	
			lower mottled sand*	
Woolwich Formation	Woolwich Beds	Woolwich Beds	Upper Shelly Clay	USC
			Laminated beds	Lb
			striped loams[1]*	
			Lower Shelly Clay	LSC
Upnor Formation	Bottom Bed	Basement Bed (of the Reading Beds)	glauconitic sand*	GS
			pebble bed *(at top)	

[1] Dewey *et al*, 1924

* units referred to but not defined in this account

2.4 STRATIGRAPHY

The three constituent formations of the Lambeth Group and their informal units are described in this section. Their distribution and relationships in the London and Hampshire basins, and detailed information covering London, is illustrated in Figures 2.3, 2.4, 2.5 and 2.6.

In the Hampshire Basin and the north-west of the London Basin the Lambeth Group rests directly on Chalk. In the south and east of the London Basin it rests on Thanet Sand, and in north Suffolk and Norfolk it overlies the Ormesby Clay (Knox *et al*, 1990) (Figure 2.1c).

The Lambeth Group is overlain by sands and pebble beds of the Harwich Formation (formerly the Blackheath and Oldhaven Beds and London Clay Basement Bed) (Ellison *et al*, 1994), which in turn is overlain by the London Clay.

The thickness of the Lambeth Group in the London Basin (see Figure 2.6a) ranges from less than 10 m in the south-east where much of it is eroded away beneath the Harwich Formation (Oldhaven and Blackheath Beds) to about 30 m in the central part of the basin, around Chertsey. In the Hampshire Basin the thickest sequence is estimated as 50 m on the Isle of Wight, but generally around 25 m and thinner in the far west.

2.4.1 Upnor Formation

The Upnor Formation was formerly known as the Bottom Bed (of the Woolwich and Reading Beds) in the London Basin, and the Basement Bed (of the Reading Beds) in the Hampshire Basin.

Distribution. See Figure 2.6f.

Boundary. The Upnor Formation is invariably at the base of the Lambeth Group (see Figures 2.3, 2.4 and 2.6). The base is well defined, with burrows extending up to 2 m below the contact. A basal bed containing flint pebbles is usually present. Where it rests on Chalk the basal bed also contains nodular unworn green-coated flints derived directly from the Chalk. These may be up to cobble grade. In the east, relatively intense bioturbation (disturbance by burrowing) has resulted in a gradational junction with the Thanet Sand. In contrast with the underlying Thanet Sand the Upnor Formation contains slightly coarser grade sand and the lower beds may be gritty and contain small (sub-millimetre) subangular flint chips. In addition there may be a weak seepage at the contact due to the silt and clay content in the Thanet Sand.

Thickness. In regional terms, in the London and Hampshire basins the thickness is generally less than 3 m. The greatest thickness, 6–7 m, occurs in parts of central London and in north Kent and Essex. In many areas it is not possible in borehole logs to identify the Upnor Formation separately from the Thanet Sand.

Lithology. The dominant lithology of the Upnor Formation in the Hampshire and London Basins is fine- to medium-grained sand and clayey sand with variable amounts of glauconite grains of fine to medium sand grade and sporadic beds or stringers of well-rounded flint pebbles. The sands are medium grey to greenish grey when fresh, weathering to pale grey-brown and yellow-brown. The glauconite grains are dark green and impart a speckled "pepper and salt" appearance. Shelly beds are seen in unweathered sections and oyster shells may occur near the base in places. In the far west of the Hampshire Basin the glauconite content declines and the flints are decomposed and associated with irregularly developed ironstone.

The Upnor Formation is best known in the London area where two units, namely glauconitic sand (GS) and pebble bed were recognised by Ellison (1991). It is proposed not to apply these units elsewhere.

In the central and eastern parts of the London Basin some of the sandy beds contain up to 25 per cent glauconite. The clay content of the Upnor Formation is variable with beds up to 300 mm thick, and laminae, of grey clay common in the east of the basin and in London.

The pebbles in the London Basin are generally less than 30 mm in diameter, but may reach 200 mm, for example around Gravesend. In central and south-east London there is a persistent pebble bed (Ellison, 1991) up to 3 m thick at the top of the formation (see Figure 2.7). It consists of well-rounded flint pebbles. At Orsett, south Essex, a wedge of pebbles up to 9 m thick occurs at the base of the formation.

Where the Upnor Formation is overlain by the Reading Formation (see Figure 2.1) the highest beds are mottled brown and purple-brown, even at depths below the level of surface weathering. In the pebble bed at the top of the Upnor Formation, a clay matrix is developed and the pebbles are brittle and red stained. Other alteration features are irregular-shaped carbonate concretions, which locally may be 0.5 m in diameter (these have been mistaken for limestones in the past), small ironstone nodules, and clay coatings on sand grains and pebbles. These secondary alterations may locally occur throughout the entire formation in the western part of the London Basin and Hampshire Basin. They are caused by pedogenic processes that operated when the deposits were close to the surface during deposition of the Reading Formation.

There is no well-developed bedding in much of the formation due to bioturbation by organisms churning up the sediment while it was being laid down. Locally, in well-bedded or laminated parts of the sequence, individual burrows are seen and sands may contain small-scale cross lamination and ripple lamination.

2.4.2   Woolwich Formation

It has long been known that there are several distinctive lithological units within the Woolwich Formation. In this account four units are described and the distribution shown on Figure 2.6.

Lower Shelly Clay (LSC)

This unit is probably the best known and easily distinguished in the Lambeth Group. It occurs principally in south-east London and north Kent, and at outcrop characteristically gives rise to finely comminuted shell debris in a clay soil.

Distribution. See Figures 2.1 and 2.6e.

Basal boundary. Everywhere it is well-defined and sharp (disconformable contact) on Lower Mottled Clay with burrows up to 10 mm in diameter extending to a depth of 1 m into the underlying strata.

Thickness. In the London Basin: up to 6 m; thickening generally from central London towards the south east. In the Hampshire Basin: about 9 m in the east at Newhaven. (Dupuis and Gruas-Cavagnetto, 1996).

Lithology. Dark grey to black clay with beds containing abundant shells, dominated by bivalves and gastropods of only two or three species. Some beds, up to 1 m, are almost entirely of shells forming a coquina; they are locally weakly cemented. An oyster-rich bed occurs locally near the base. A few beds, of brownish grey clay, are slightly cemented with siderite. Finely comminuted carbonaceous debris, some of which may be pyritised, occurs in places. In the London Basin beds of medium-grained sand become increasingly frequent towards the east.

Laminated beds

This unit is equivalent to the "laminated sands and silts" of Ellison (1991).

Distribution. Recognised only in the south-east part of the London Basin (Figure 2.6d and 2.7), but similar beds occur in association with the Lower Shelly Clay at Newhaven in the Hampshire Basin.

Basal boundary. Usually a rapid gradation with Lower Shelly Clay.

Thickness. Generally less than 4 m but up to 9 m south of Stratford.

Lithology. A thinly interbedded succession of fine to medium sand, silt and clay with scattered intact bivalve shells. Beds are generally less than 50 mm thick and typically finely laminated on a millimetre scale. Lenticular bedding, ripple lamination, burrows and some bioturbated, structureless, beds are usual. Localised bodies of sand (probable channels) up to about 4 m thick occur, particularly around Lambeth and Bermondsey in south-east London. Sands are more extensive between Docklands and Stratford. Typically the sand is pale olive to pale brown, medium-grained, well sorted and cross laminated, with some clay drapes and scattered bivalves. Thin beds of colour mottled clay and silt, interpreted as Upper Mottled Clay of the Reading Formation, occur within the Laminated beds between Docklands and Stratford.

Included in the Laminated beds is a sequence known as striped loams (Dewey *et al*, 1924). These beds were formerly exposed at Loam Pit Hill, Lewisham and include clays that contain leaf fossils. It is probable that these beds occupy an erosional hollow cut into the main thickness of the Laminated beds (Figures 2.5 and 2.7).

Upper Shelly Clay (USC)

Distribution. Mainly in south London between Westminster and Bermondsey in the north, to Mitcham and Lewisham in the south (Figure 2.6c). There are also outliers of the Upper Shelly Clay proved in boreholes south-east of the main area and to the north-west, in Essex. It seems likely that these occurrences are in shallow channels in the top part of the Lambeth Group.

Basal boundary. Sharp (disconformable) contact on Upper Mottled Clay or sharp contact or rapid gradation into Laminated beds.

Thickness. Probably no more than 3 m. In many borehole records it may have been classified as shelly basal beds of London Clay.

Lithology. Grey shelly clay, thinly interbedded with grey brown silt and very fine sand. A greater number of bivalve species than in the Lower Shelly Clay are present sporadically throughout. In the south-east of the area the beds are generally of sand (Figure 2.6c). The unit is generally thinly laminated. It includes weakly cemented shell beds (up to 0.43 m thick) containing Ostrea, bioturbated sand beds, sands and silts with rip-up clay clasts (less than 5 mm) and clays and silts with sand-filled burrows. Scattered glauconite grains may occur throughout. A limestone bed, generally 0.1–0.3 m thick (the maximum recorded thickness is 1.89 m) known as the *Paludina* Limestone, forms a significant marker bed that is probably persistent in the area between Bermondsey and Lewisham. It is a fossiliferous grey calcisiltite with an earthy texture. It contains unbroken and comminuted gastropods, the latter in the basal 30 mm.

2.4.3 Reading Formation

Distribution. Occurs throughout the Hampshire Basin and in all but the south-east of the London Basin. In London the formation divides into two leaves separated by Woolwich Formation (Figures 2.5 and 2.7). The leaves are termed the Upper Mottled Clay and the Lower Mottled Clay. In areas where the Woolwich Formation does not intervene it is not possible, using lithological criteria, to identify the two leaves. However, when current biostratigraphical research is completed it may be possible to discriminate them using fossil spores.

Basal boundary. The base of undivided Reading Formation and the base of the Lower Mottled Clay (overlying the Upnor Formation) is usually diffuse and difficult to place precisely because of clay translocation and colour mottling caused by pedogenic processes affecting the top of the Upnor Formation. The Upper Mottled Clay generally rests on Laminated beds, this contact also being difficult to place due to diffuse colour mottling. The Upper Mottled Clay interdigitates with the Laminated beds in the Stratford area of London.

Lithology. Clay is the dominant lithology in the Reading Formation. The bulk of the formation consists of largely unbedded, colour-mottled silty clay and clay. This lithology is the principal characteristic of the Reading Beds or plastic clay of former authors. Colours include pale brown and pale grey-blue, dark brown, pale green , red-brown and crimson depending on the oxidation state of the sediments. The clays contain numerous fissures, many of them spoon-shaped (listric) and polished, which give rise to a blocky texture.

Beds of silt and sand may constitute up to 50 per cent of the formation. Their dominant colour is brown, red hues being less prevalent than in the clays. Many of these beds are thinly laminated with small burrows and root traces, and minor brecciation caused by soft sediment deformation has been noted. Beds of well-sorted fine to medium-grained sand also occur sporadically throughout the Reading Formation, mainly in the west of the London Basin and the Hampshire Basin. Their three-dimensional structure is not known in detail but they appear to fill steep-sided channels, perhaps in the order of 100–200 m wide and up to 4 m deep.

Detailed examination of borehole core in the undivided Reading Formation, the Upper Mottled Clay, and to a lesser extent the Lower Mottled Clay, reveals a series of small fining upwards cycles. At the base of each unit is a laminated sand or silt with minor burrowing and locally ripple lamination. It passes up into mottled clays, brecciated in places, with root traces, and culminates in mottled clay with carbonate nodules.

In the west of the London Basin and the Hampshire Basin thin, black, carbonaceous clays are recorded locally in the middle of the sequence. These may be roughly at the horizon of the Lower Shelly Clay (see Figure 2.4). Also in the west of the Hampshire Basin, red mottled clays, identical in lithology to the Reading Formation are known as the West Park Farm Member of the London Clay (see Figure 2.4) (Bristow *et al*, 1991).

The Lower Mottled Clay contains carbonate nodules up to 0.5 m in diameter particularly in the top part. They may be hard and splintery or softer and powdery. Exceptionally, in east London, they have coalesced to form a massive limestone up to 1.6 m thick. Purple hues are a feature of the Lower Mottled Clay and minor amounts of irregularly iron-cemented and partially cemented calcareous clayey sands are recorded locally in east London. Sands become increasingly dominant east of London and may be referred to as lower mottled sand. Farther east, in Essex and Kent, it passes into a pale grey-brown to purple-brown structureless medium to coarse-grained sand. In places in north Kent this is iron-cemented and known locally as the Winterbourne Ironstone. It was informally referred to as ferruginous sand by Ellison (1983).

The Upper Mottled Clay is not distinguished lithologically either from the Lower Mottled Clay or the main bulk of undivided Reading Formation. It is identified simply as an upper leaf of the Formation lying above the Lower Shelly Clay. In cores in central and east London it consists largely of mottled clays, silty clays and silts with colours similar to those of the Lower Mottled Clay, the only exception being the absence of purple hues.

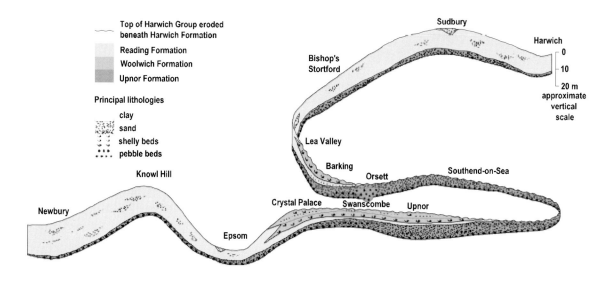

Figure 2.3   *Schematic section showing the variation in the Lambeth Group, London Basin (© NERC)*

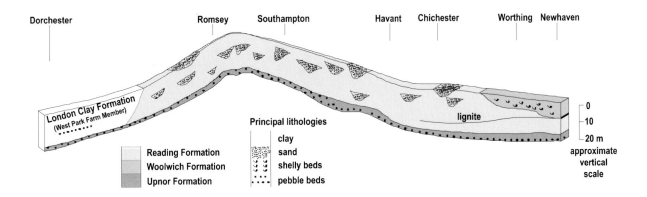

Figure 2.4 *Schematic section showing the variation in the Lambeth Group, Hampshire Basin (© NERC)*

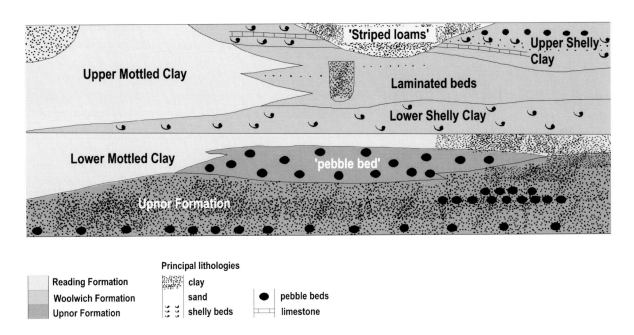

Figure 2.5 *Generalised Lambeth Group succession in central London (© NERC)*

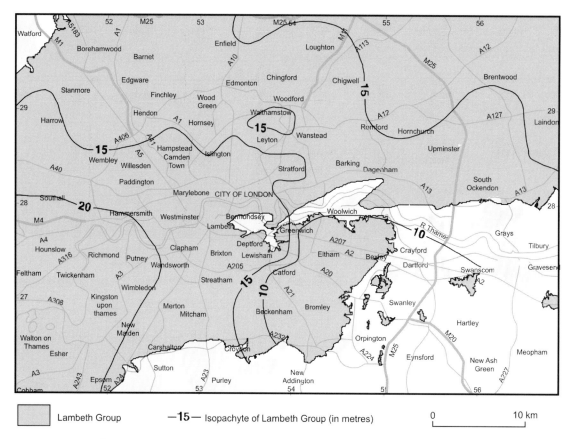

Lambeth Group   —15— Isopachyte of Lambeth Group (in metres)   0   10 km

Figure 2.6a *Distribution of Lambeth Group units in London: thickness of Lambeth Group (© NERC)*

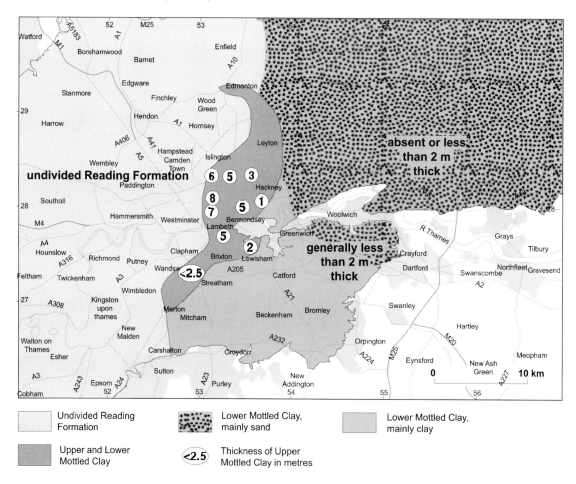

	Undivided Reading Formation		Lower Mottled Clay, mainly sand		Lower Mottled Clay, mainly clay
	Upper and Lower Mottled Clay	<2.5	Thickness of Upper Mottled Clay in metres		

Figure 2.6b *Distribution of Lambeth Group units in London: thicknesses of Reading Formation undivided and the Upper Mottled Clay and Lower Mottled Clay (© NERC)*

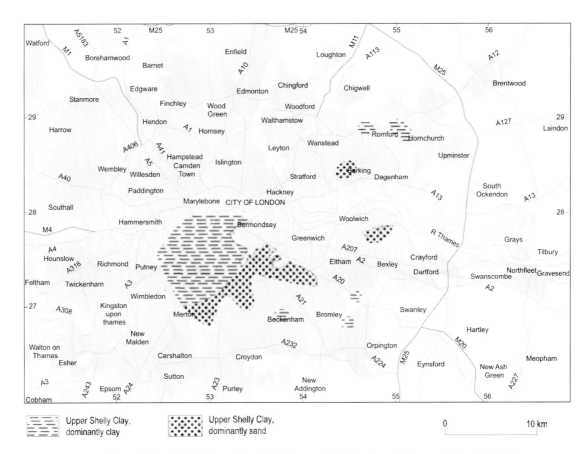

Upper Shelly Clay, dominantly clay

Upper Shelly Clay, dominantly sand

0   10 km

Figure 2.6c *Distribution of Lambeth Group units in London: thickness of Upper Shelly Clay (© NERC)*

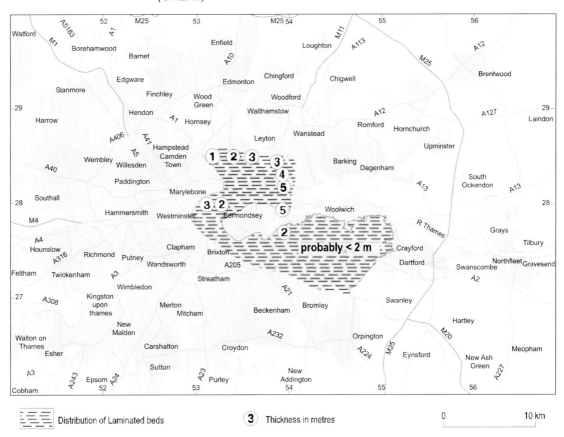

Distribution of Laminated beds

3 Thickness in metres

0   10 km

Figure 2.6d *Distribution of Lambeth Group units in London: thickness of Laminated beds (© NERC)*

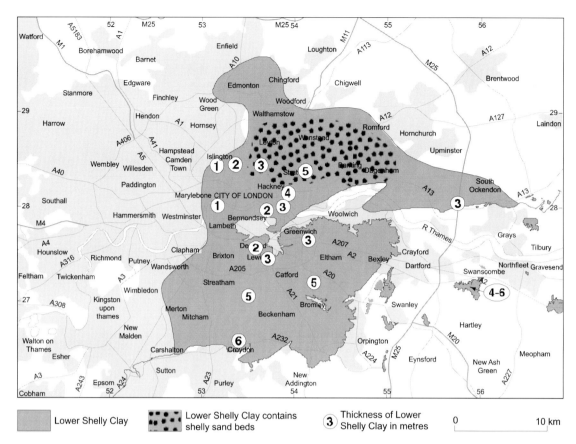

Lower Shelly Clay

Lower Shelly Clay contains shelly sand beds

③ **Thickness of Lower Shelly Clay in metres**

0   10 km

Figure 2.6e *Distribution of Lambeth Group units in London: thickness of Lower Shelly Clay (© NERC)*

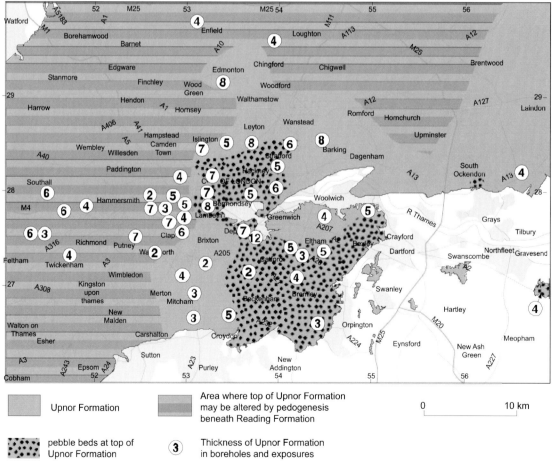

Upnor Formation

Area where top of Upnor Formation may be altered by pedogenesis beneath Reading Formation

pebble beds at top of Upnor Formation

③ **Thickness of Upnor Formation in boreholes and exposures**

0   10 km

Figure 2.6f *Distribution of Lambeth Group units in London: thickness of Upnor Formation (© NERC)*

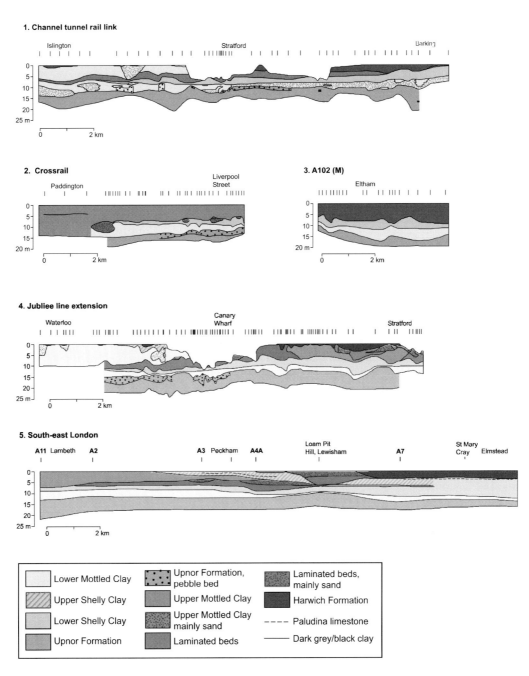

Figure 2.7   *Sections through Lambeth Group deposits: (1) Channel Tunnel Rail Link, (2) Crossrail, (3) A102(M), (4) Jubilee Line Extension, (5) south-east London (© NERC)*

2.5   DEPOSITIONAL ENVIRONMENT AND PROCESSES

Typical photographs of cores and exposures of the different units that make up the Lambeth Group are presented in Appendix 2.

The Upnor Formation was deposited in a shallow sea (< 20 m water depth), in which sedimentation was influenced by tidal flows. A reduction in sea level, possibly combined with uplift, led to emergence and establishment of a terrestrial environment in which the Reading Formation was laid down on marshy mudflats, which formed an alluvial plain crossed by river channels. The prevailing climate had high temperatures and pronounced wet and dry seasons. Sub-tropical subaerial weathering occurred and soil forming processes (pedogenesis) affected the sediments, including the Upnor Formation, where this was close to the ground surface. This was particularly intense at the top of the Lower Mottled Clay, in the east of the London Basin, where calcrete and ferricrete precipitation took place during a major hiatus in deposition (the mid-Lambeth Group hiatus of Page, 1994).

In the east of the London Basin, a transgressive event then led to the deposition of the Lower Shelly Clay and Laminated beds of the Woolwich Formation in a brackish-water lagoonal or estuarine environment. Also in the east of the basin, a second emergent phase and return to a terrestrial environment led to deposition of the Upper Mottled Clay, overlying the Woolwich Formation. A further transgression was responsible for the formation of the Upper Shelly Clay in central and southern London.

The sediments laid down in these alternating conditions are preserved mainly in central London, and locally in the east of the Hampshire Basin. The transgressive events did not reach far into the west of the London Basin, and in the east much of the succession was removed by erosion prior to deposition of the Harwich Formation and London Clay.

Processes active during deposition included bioturbation, pedogenesis and weathering. Each of these has given rise to distinctive structures and lithologies within the Lambeth Group.

Burrows of various types occur throughout the Lambeth Group. They are comparatively uncommon in the Reading Formation and Woolwich Formation but a particularly strong burrowed horizon occurs at the junction between the Lower Mottled Clay and the Lower Shelly Clay, coincident with the Mid-Lambeth Group hiatus. Bioturbation is prevalent only in the Upnor Formation.

Pedogenic processes in a sub-tropical climate affected the Upnor Formation, and the Upper and Lower Mottled Clay. These processes involved dissolution, precipitation, transport, oxidation and reduction associated with fluctuating water tables, and reduction associated with root development. The processes led to:

- colour mottling due to varying degrees of oxidation
- clay enrichment caused by downward migration of clay into sands, resulting in clay coatings developing on sand grains and pebbles
- dissolution of shells and removal of organic material by oxidation
- the formation of duricrusts caused by precipitation of carbonate cements derived from the dissolution of shells. The form of carbonate cementing depended on the local permeability, and proximity of sources of cementing agents. Carbonate cement forms a weak cement locally in the Upnor Formation pebble bed, a hard limestone (particularly in the vicinity of the shell beds), and calcrete nodules particularly in the Lower Mottled Clay. Calcrete occurs as fine to medium gravel-sized powdery concretions in the sandier Lower Mottled Clay in east London. Large nodules and more extensive carbonate cementing in irregular masses up to 1 m thick, occurs also in the Lower Mottled Clay. Examples of these calcretes are shown in Figures 4.3 and 4.4. Locally in north London, sandy beds in the base of the Lower Mottled Clay or at the top of the Upnor Formation contain silica cemented beds, interpreted as silcretes, formed during pedogenesis. The best known of these is the Hertfordshire Puddingstone. Ferricretes are recorded rarely, usually in strata close below the base of the Lower Shelly Clay, also caused by emergence at the mid Lambeth Group hiatus (for example, at Newhaven).

Fissures with polished and slickensided surfaces have developed as a result of syndepositional desiccation during seasonal changes in ground moisture in the mottled clays. Relatively minor amounts of fissuring occur also in the clays of the Woolwich Formation.

2.6 GEOPHYSICAL LOG CHARACTERISTICS

Downhole geophysical logs are helpful for correlating Lambeth Group successions proved in boreholes, particularly when they are calibrated with a continuous core. Used in this way they are of considerable assistance in determining the lithological units present where no core has been taken or where core is not recovered.

In general terms the gamma ray log has been most commonly used. The neutron trace is thought to be the next most useful, particularly in the Reading Formation where it responds well to sand bodies (Whitaker *et al*, 1985).

An example of a gamma log taken in a representative central London borehole for which full core was available is shown on Figure 2.8. The boundaries of the units were defined in the core.

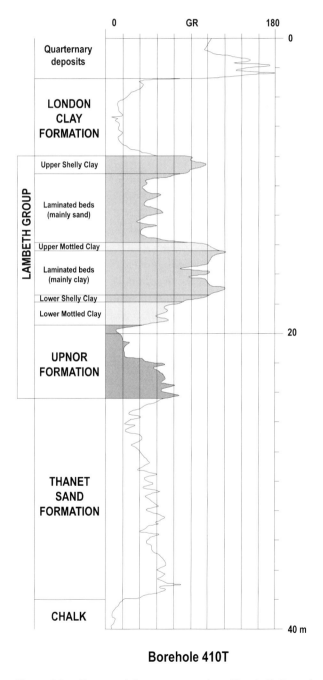

Borehole 410T

Figure 2.8   *Representative gamma ray log of Lambeth Group in central London (© NERC)*

2.7　MINERALOGY

There are no systematic studies of the mineralogy of the Lambeth Group but some trends can be inferred from published material. A generalised clay minerals profile through a typical Lambeth Group sequence in central London is shown on Figure 2.9.

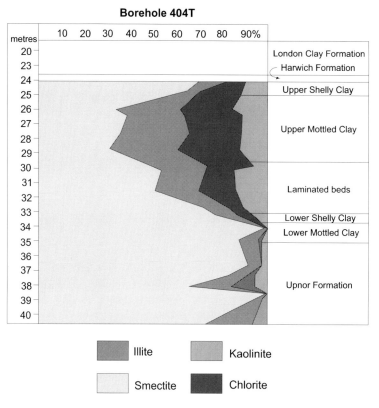

Figure 2.9　*Generalised clay mineralogy profile of Lambeth Group in central London (© NERC)*

2.7.1　Upnor Formation

The non-clay minerals are dominated by quartz, with up to 30 per cent glauconite grains. The quartz grains are generally well-rounded to sub-rounded but with some evidence of corrosion. The glauconite grains vary from well-rounded to angular and weather at outcrop to goethite or ilmenite. Samples from the northern outcrops of the London Basin (Bateman and Moffat, 1987) also contain grains of feldspar, quartzite, ironstone, chert chalcedony and pyrite.

Clay minerals are largely in the sand matrix and constitute up to 50 per cent of the Upnor Formation. In the Hampshire Basin and more eastern parts of the London Basin smectite is the dominant clay, with illite and a little or no kaolinite. Mixed layer illite-smectite is also present. The smectite is generally well-crystallised and derived from the weathering of ash falls from volcanoes active mainly during deposition of the Upnor Formation. In the west and north of the London Basin illite is usually the dominant clay mineral and kaolinite also tends to become more common (Gilkes, 1968; Bateman and Moffat, 1987; Ellison and Lake, 1986). There are also a few thin beds (less than 10 mm) containing a particularly high proportion of smectite which may indicate relatively un-reworked volcanic ash.

2.7.2   Woolwich Formation

Little mineralogical information is available on the Woolwich Formation. High levels of organic material are found in the Laminated beds in particular. Thin lignite beds are recorded from several places, in the east of the Hampshire Basin and in the London Basin, associated with the Laminated beds and at the base of the Lower Shelly Clay. Iron minerals such as pyrite, magnetite and limonite occur at several horizons. The ferruginous sands, in the east of the London Basin are locally silicified, suggesting leaching and iron segregation in conditions of a variable water table.

The clay minerals in the more sandy beds are generally dominated by kaolinite, whereas clay beds contain illite, smectite and kaolinite (Blondeau and Pomerol, 1968).

2.7.3   Reading Formation

Quartz, from sand to clay grade, is usually the dominant non-clay mineral of the Reading Formation. Mica and feldspar are minor components. The composition of the few percent of iron minerals is dependent on the redox conditions during and immediately following deposition. Jarosite, haematite, limonite, collophane and magnetite/ilmenite may also be present in the oxidised zones; pyrite occurs in some clays dominated by grey hues.

The lower part of the undivided Reading Formation in Essex and the Lower Mottled Clay in London has a smectite-dominated clay mineral assemblage, similar to the Upnor Formation. In contrast, the Upper Mottled Clay and the top part of the undivided Reading Formation is dominated by illite with less smectite and some kaolinite that appears to replace smectite in places (Ellison and Lake, 1986).

In the Hampshire Basin the Reading Formation on the Isle of Wight contains mainly illite and kaolinite, smectite becoming abundant only in the top of the formation (Gilkes, 1968; Buurman, 1980). Regional trends in the Hampshire Basin suggest that smectite increases generally towards the north and west (BGS unpublished data), although it may occur in relatively high proportions in specific bands, reflecting its primary origin as ash falls. However, weathering of the ashes in an environment, which led to the formation of strongly red mottled clays of the Reading Formation is more likely to give rise to kaolinite rather than smectite.

2.8   POST-DEPOSITIONAL FEATURES

The principal post-depositional influences on the Lambeth Group are tectonic forces, glacial and periglacial processes, and changing groundwater level. In areas of outcrop, surface weathering effects also may have modified the deposits.

2.8.1   Structural features

The Lambeth Group has been gently folded on a regional scale and the beds in the majority of the London and Hampshire Basins dip generally at less than 1°. Steep dips, greater than 45° occur along the Hogs Back and in the Isle of Wight. In these areas the Lambeth Group, mainly Reading Formation may contain shear planes and minor faults. Steep dips have also been recorded in association with the Greenwich Fault in south-east London such as in the open, upright folds, probably associated with disturbance close to the fault in south London (Bromehead, 1922).

Also in London the Tertiary strata and Chalk are broken by small faults trending NW–SE, probably with throws less than 2 m. These are rarely recorded but are inferred from an evaluation of the regional structure and hydrogeological models.

2.8.2 Features related to glaciation

Glacial disturbance of the Lambeth Group is a potential issue only in outcrops and subcrop (occurrences below drift deposits) in north Essex and Suffolk. There is no specific information on this but it is possible that release of high hydrostatic pressure beneath an ice margin may have caused disruption of bedding in sands within the Lambeth Group.

2.8.3 Features related to periglaciation

Periglacial conditions existed in southern England during at least two glacial episodes in the past 500 000 years. The thinly bedded nature of the Lambeth Group, in particular the presence of water-bearing sands, resulted in a relatively high susceptibility to disturbance caused by ground ice and cryoturbation.

Pingos, large dome-shaped bodies of ground ice developed below the ground surface, grow by the progressive addition of water, probably under artesian pressure. Melting of pingos is thought to be at least partly responsible for more than 25 anomalously deep subsurface depressions in the rockhead beneath London (Hutchinson, 1980). Associated with some of these hollows are masses of Lambeth Group sediments that have been injected, under high hydrostatic pressure, through the London Clay into the base of the hollow. Artesian groundwater conditions formerly occurred in much of the central part of the London Basin, and therefore potentially there is the possibility that there are undiscovered areas of similarly disturbed Lambeth Group.

Modification of the Lambeth Group at outcrop by active-layer processes such as cryoturbation is largely unstudied. It is likely to have resulted in the development of small scale structures such as involutions and the diapiric injection of sands. These features may be particularly well developed in interbedded sand and clay because of the potential contrast in the freezing point of groundwater in coarser compared to fine grained sediments, dependent on the relative pore pressures. Slopes formed of the clay-dominated Reading Formation owe their present form to periglacial slope processes and are likely to be mantled by 1–3 m of Head deposits containing shear surfaces, aligned roughly parallel to the ground surface. Immediately beneath the Head, periglacially weathered clay is generally brecciated and softer than the clay beneath (see for example Spink, 1991). Periglacial shearing of the Reading Formation is likely to be exacerbated by the presence of pre-existing shears in the mottled clays.

Valley bulging is broad anticlinal deformation of strata, under periglacial conditions, underlying valley floors. It is commonly associated with clay-dominated strata and is likely to affect all valleys that have been rapidly incised. This releases large horizontal stresses, which under favourable conditions may be sufficient to initiate lateral deformation of the deposits towards the valley axis.

2.8.4 Features due to Chalk dissolution

The Chalk dissolves to give a karstic surface with pipes and swallow holes up to several metres deep. The most significant dissolution has occurred at the margin of overlying impermeable deposits where surface drainage is concentrated, for example close to the junction with the Lambeth Group. Although many of the dissolution features are filled with superficial deposits, it is likely that, particularly close to the edge of the outcrops, the Lambeth Group, and the underlying Thanet Sand, are let down into Chalk dissolution features.

2.8.5   The effect of rising groundwater

The current rise in groundwater levels in London, caused by a reduction in water abstraction, is well documented (see for example Environment Agency, 1997). It has an influence on the Lambeth Group because the sandy Upnor Formation is regarded as being in hydrogeological continuity with the underlying Thanet Sand and the Chalk. Historically, these sandy Tertiary beds together have been known as the Basal Sands aquifer.

The abstraction of water from the aquifer, starting in the early part of the 19th century, led to a fall in groundwater levels in the central region of the basin (Water Resources Board, 1972). Consequently the top of the Chalk was probably dewatered over an area of several square kilometres in the centre of the basin (Lucas and Robinson, 1995).

The recovery of groundwater levels in London has several implications, which were considered in CIRIA SP69 (Simpson *et al*, 1989). Basements or tunnels excavated above the water table and not sealed against the ingress of water would be subject to flooding. Sealed structures submerged by rising water would become buoyant and liable to uplift pressures detrimental to stability. Structures originally below the water table might not be sufficiently watertight to contend with increased hydrostatic head and remedial sealing or continuous pumping would be required.

Tunnels are already suffering from increased seepage, and chemical attack. One example is on the London Underground Northern Line, where very acidic waters caused deterioration of the tunnel linings south of Old Street station. Investigations there suggested that the source of the acid was oxidised pyrite in sands in the Lambeth Group, probably in the Laminated beds. These beds had originally been saturated, but subsequently dewatered as the water table was lowered. The pyrite was subsequently oxidised by air from the railway tunnels, in particular by the piston effect of passing trains and by changes in barometric pressure. Water seeping from the overlying London Clay, resulted in the production of highly acidic, aggressive groundwater (Robins *et al*, 1997). As the water table rises, increasing amounts of oxidised pyrite will give rise to potentially corrosive acidic groundwater (Rainey and Rosenbaum, 1989).

During conditions of falling water table, the resultant underdrainage and consolidation of strata resulted in the lowering of the ground surface in central London by several hundred millimetres. It also increased the bearing strength of the London Clay and clays in the Lambeth Group. As a result of rising groundwater, increases in pore water pressure and the swelling of clay may result in a reduction in shear strength, and hence bearing capacity.

3   Engineering hazards

3.1   UNCERTAINTIES STEMMING FROM THE GEOLOGY

Some of the uncertainties about the Lambeth Group as a whole are the:

- highly variable conditions throughout
- permeability contrast between adjacent sand layers
- difficulty of interpreting piezometric profiles
- difficulty of obtaining good undisturbed samples for geotechnical testing.

In terms of specific units in the Lambeth Group, these uncertainties are summarised in Table 3.1.

Table 3.1   *Summary of engineering issues that relate to lithological units of the Lambeth Group*

	Upper Mottled Clay and Lower Mottled Clay	Upper Shelly Clay	Lower Shelly Clay	Laminated beds	Upnor formation
General heterogeneity		●	●	●	●
Lithological					
Sand-filled channels	●	●			
Hard bands	●	●	●	●	●
Pebble beds				●	●
Lignite			●	●	
Water					
Perched water	●	●		●	
Variation in groundwater regime	●	●	●	●	●
Mineralogy					
Glauconite					●
Gypsum			●		
Pyrite		●	●	●	
Smectite	●				●
Post depositional					
Chalk dissolution features					●
Features of periglacial origin	●	●	●	●	●
Other					
Fissuring	●				
Gases					●

These are amplified in terms of potential hazards for engineering construction in the following sections.

3.2 ENGINEERING HAZARDS

The Lambeth Group can present significant engineering hazards, which may not be fully appreciated during the planning of a project and yet may remain through the whole life of the project. Expedients are required in design and construction to allow for variation in the hazard to reduce the residual risk to a project. The potential problem, occurrence and cause of each engineering hazard is summarised in this section of the report.

General heterogeneity

Potential problem	The Lambeth Group contains a great variety of lithologies, including weak rock, gravel, sand, silt and low to very high plasticity clays, which vary vertically through the sequence and geographically. Interbedded clays, sands and silts exist on a macro- and meso-scale.
Occurrence	At various levels. Intra-formational variation and intra-unit variation exists. Lithological units are diachronous.
Cause	Significant changes in relative sea level during deposition causing a shift in depositional environment and resulting in major vertical and lateral variation; affected by different post-depositional processes. Displacement of the strata by faulting causes juxtaposition of different lithologies.

Lithological – sand-filled channels

Potential problem	Rapid and unpredicted change in ground conditions; sand bodies may be water-bearing; tend to be steep-sided and laterally impersistent.
Occurrence	Occur throughout the Lambeth Group. Particularly a problem where they occur within clay stratum. Particularly prevalent in the Reading Formation, west of central London and in the Laminated beds.
Cause	Channels represent non-migrating watercourses cutting across alluvial plain.

Lithological – hard bands (calcretes, silcretes, shelly limestones)

Potential problem	Obstruction to boring, drilling, piling or excavation activity.
Occurrence	Various stratigraphical horizons; impersistent; variable strength.
Cause	Presence of reef builders, eg oysters during deposition. Early post-depositional cementation due to pedogenesis (duricrusts, hard clays). Geochemical fronts due to groundwater movement (iron pan). Cementation of calcareous-rich material.

Lithological – pebble beds

Potential problem	Form of hard band, particularly abrasive due to concentration of flint gravel. Water-bearing. Sometimes cemented with carbonate (calcrete) or silica (silcrete – eg Hertfordshire Puddingstone).
Occurrence	Predominantly within the Upnor Formation, although occur at base of overlying Thames Group (eg Harwich Formation [Blackheath Beds], not strictly Lambeth Group, but often associated with problems with the group). Notable pebble bed occurs at the top of the Upnor Formation in London up to 3 m thick.
Cause	Deposition in high-energy environment, associated with tidal channels or shallowing of sea. Base of transgressive deposits.

Lithological – lignite

Potential problem	Variable strength. Trees and large roots preserved *in situ* may prove an obstacle to construction. Where bedded, strong fabric may be preserved.
Occurrence	Associated with the Woolwich Formation or hiatuses. Pyritised timber material often found in sand channel structures. Notable lignitic horizons occur in North Kent (Shorne outlier) and along the South Coast.
Cause	Allochthonous (found in a place other than where they and their constituents were formed) and autochthonous (originating or formed in the place where found) forms are both present.

Water – perched water

Potential problem	Presence of laminations or beds of water-bearing sand, silt or gravel.
Occurrence	Associated with the presence of granular units.
	Particularly characteristic of the Woolwich Formation (Upper Shelly Clay, Laminated beds, Lower Shelly Clay).
	Occurs at interface with London Clay (eg Blackheath Beds) and Thanet Sand Formation.
Cause	Various. Deposition in a tidal, fluvial channel or coarse clastic marine environment. Associated with base of transgression.

Water – variation in the groundwater regime

Potential problem   *Groundwater rise.* Swelling of clay minerals may lead to differential movements, additional loads and damage to structures. Reduced bearing capacity. Water ingress in buried structures. Buoyancy of sealed structures.
Groundwater fall. Shrinkage of clay minerals may result in subsidence due to desiccation, depletion of O_2 from atmospheres created in sand strata, oxidation of deleterious minerals.

Occurrence   Locally or regionally.

Cause   Local dewatering, consequence of changes in regional abstraction of the deep aquifer, leakage from drains/water supply, tree root action.

Mineralogy – glauconite, gypsum, pyrite

Potential problem   Weathering may release reaction products that are aggressive to materials. Minerals known to cause problems include pyrite (FeS), glauconite (complex Fe/K rich clay mineral) and gypsum ($CaSO_4.2H_2O$). Pyrite in the presence of calcium carbonate and bacteria forms sulphuric acid. Glauconite oxidises to limonite or goethite with the potential resultant depletion of O_2 from enclosed atmospheres. Gypsum may be a source of sulphuric acid.

Occurrence   Pyrite occurs disseminated within dark-coloured clay lithologies and within unoxidised sands within the Woolwich and Reading Formations.

Glauconite occurs solely within the Upnor Formation. Gypsum is known to have formed within the sediments of the Woolwich Formation but is also a product of the weathering of mud rocks.

Cause   Pyrite forms in anoxic environments often within the sediment due to the presence of decomposing organic matter. Glauconite forms almost exclusively within a marine environment. Gypsum may form as a result of the weathering of pyrite-bearing mud rocks but may also form in the sediment where evaporation is high.

Mineralogy – smectite

Potential problem   Smectite is a clay mineral (Na montmorillonite) with a high cation exchange capacity and can undergo large volumetric changes.

Occurrence   As thin layers (< 20 mm thick) or disseminated throughout the sediment.

Cause   Volcanic ash fall material.

Post-depositional – chalk solution features

Potential problem   Subsidence or collapse of Lambeth Group materials into void created by dissolution of underlying Chalk. Dissolution features (karst) vary in size and form.

Occurrence   Distribution controlled by presence of permeable materials overlying Chalk and structural discontinuities in the chalk.

Cause   Influenced by factors including: thickness of cover, groundwater movement and geochemistry (acidity may promote dissolution), geological structure.

Post-depositional – features of periglacial origin

Potential problem   Some features of periglacial origin may pose an engineering hazard; these have been reviewed by Hutchinson (1980). The major features include frost stirring and sorting, frost cracking (brecciation), landslides, solifluction, pingos, valley disturbances, anomalies beneath river terraces.

Occurrence   Local and regional.

Cause   Glacial and periglacial conditions existed within southern England during the Pleistocene.

Fissuring

Potential problem   Responsible for reduced strength of medium to high-plasticity clays, instability of cuts in clay, potential pathway for water.

Occurrence   Mottled clays within the Reading Formation, clays within the Woolwich Formation.

Cause   Various: desiccation of sediment during pedogenesis, dewatering during burial, tectonic disturbance, stress relief due to unloading.

Gases

Potential problem   De-oxygenation of air and relative enrichment in other gases.

Occurrence   Currently known to occur within dewatered sand strata due to temporarily or transient lowered groundwater levels.

Cause   Condition is thought to be due to the oxidation of minerals, particularly glauconite.

The above hazards essentially stem from the geological origins and nature of the variety of materials that comprise the Lambeth Group. In Chapter 4, the presentation of engineering properties of these materials is linked to the geological subdivisions. The implications of the above hazards and relevance of the engineering properties for construction are examined in Chapter 5. Investigation has to provide the information needed first to allow hazards to be recognised and their risks assessed and secondly the relevant engineering properties determined. Thus Chapter 6 on ground investigation links back to the above hazards and to the next chapter.

4   Engineering properties

4.1   SOURCES OF DATA FOR LONDON BASIN

Data on the engineering properties of the units that make up the Lambeth Group have been drawn from ground investigations carried out for the following major projects in the London Basin.

Jubilee Line Extension (JLE)

This 15.5 km extension to the Jubilee Line runs underground from Green Park, in central London, eastwards to Canning Town, and thence as a surface railway to Stratford in east London (see Figures 4.1 and 4.2(a)). Twenty-eight per cent of the running tunnels have been constructed wholly in the Lambeth Group, and it has influenced the design and construction of six underground stations, the foundations to two surface stations and a new depot building at Stratford Market. Both the depth and thickness of the Lambeth Group varies along the route. At Green Park, the top of the Lambeth Group is 52 m bgl; at Westminster station, it is 46 m bgl and between 18.6 m and 19.8 m thick; at London Bridge station, it is 28 m bgl and 17 m thick; at Bermondsey station, which was constructed wholly in the Lambeth Group, it is 9 m bgl and 16 m thick; at Canada Water station, it is 9 m bgl and 11 m thick; at Canary Wharf, it is 12 m bgl and 8 m thick; at North Greenwich, the Lambeth Group underlies 11 m of London Clay and is 24 m bgl and 17 m thick. The site investigation for the JLE has been described by Linney and Page (1996).

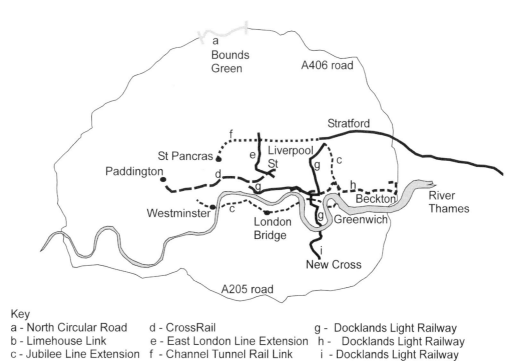

Key
a - North Circular Road   d - CrossRail   g - Docklands Light Railway
b - Limehouse Link   e - East London Line Extension h - Docklands Light Railway
c - Jubilee Line Extension   f - Channel Tunnel Rail Link   i - Docklands Light Railway

Figure 4.1 *Location of recent and proposed projects involving construction in Lambeth Group in London Basin*

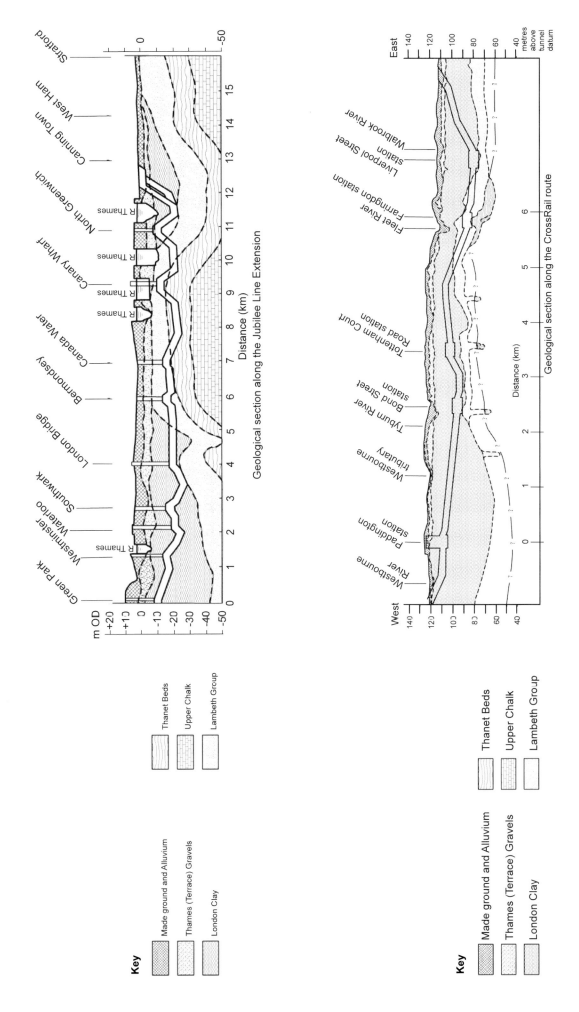

Key

Thanet Beds
Upper Chalk
Lambeth Group

Made ground and Alluvium
Thames (Terrace) Gravels
London Clay

Geological section along the Jubilee Line Extension

Geological section along the CrossRail route

48

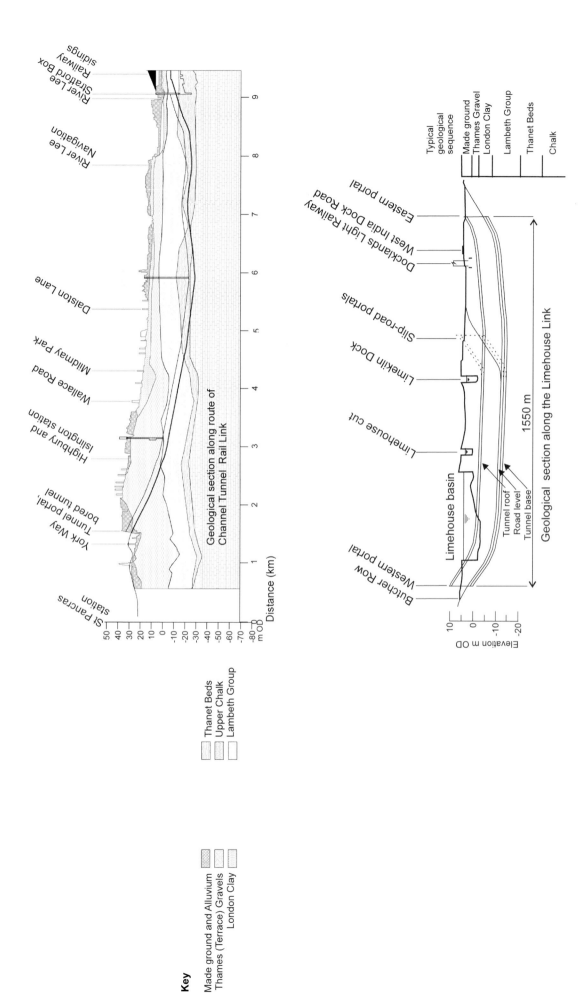

Key

Made ground and Alluvium
Thames (Terrace) Gravels
London Clay

Thanet Beds
Upper Chalk
Lambeth Group

Figure 4.2   Cross-sections along new railway and road routes in the London Basin: (a) Jubilee Line Extension, (b) Crossrail, (c) Channel Tunnel Rail Link, (d) Limehouse Link

Crossrail

Construction of an underground railway beneath the centre of London, linking the mainline termini of Paddington and Liverpool Street, has been proposed and a ground investigation has been carried out along the route (Lehane *et al*, 1995). The investigation included the definition of the geological and engineering characteristics of the Lambeth Group, in which some tunnelling and basement construction is proposed. The top of the Lambeth Group varies between 10 m and 30 m bgl along the route (see Figures 4.1 and 4.2(b)).

Channel Tunnel Rail Link (CTRL)

The Channel Tunnel Rail Link (CTRL) will be a new 108 km railway between London and the Channel Tunnel near Folkestone. CTRL's London terminal will be in a refurbished and extended St Pancras Station. An overview of the initial ground investigation for CTRL has been given by Beckwith *et al* (1996).

Underground construction within the Lambeth Group has been involved in Section 2, which comprises London Tunnels East and West and Stratford Box. London Tunnels West pass from St Pancras Station, under Islington and Hackney to Stratford Station. London Tunnels East pass from Stratford Station under Barking and emerge at ground surface at Ripple Lane Junction, near Dagenham.

A geological cross-section along the route is shown in Figure 4.2(c). At the western end of the tunnels, in central London, about 25–35 m of London Clay overlies a thin layer of the permeable Harwich Formation and the Lambeth Group which is 15–20 m thick. Towards Stratford Station, the London Clay reduces to about 5–10 m thickness and the Lambeth Group remains about 20 m thick. In the vicinity of the River Lea and River Thames, ie towards Stratford Station and as far east as the A406 North Circular Road, the London Clay and the top of the Lambeth Group have been eroded. The Lambeth Group is about 10 m thick and is overlain by river terrace gravels and recent flood plain deposits. The London Clay reappears in Barking and overlies the Harwich Formation (approximately 5 m thick) and the Lambeth Group (approximately 15 m thick).

Limehouse Link

The Limehouse Link road tunnel, which forms part of a new highway connecting the London Docklands development area to the City of London, was completed in 1993 (De Moor and Stevenson, 1996). The tunnel was constructed along two-thirds of the 1.6 km length by top-down cut-and-cover techniques, through made ground, alluvium, terrace gravels, the London Clay and into the Lambeth Group. The maximum depth of excavation was 20 m bgl, with the top of the Lambeth Group between 11m and 14.5 m bgl; the roof of the completed tunnel generally lies at 6–8 m bgl (see Figure 4.2(d)).

Waterloo International Terminal (WIT)

Waterloo International Terminal in London was opened in 1993. It was constructed over part of the existing railway station at Waterloo. At the site, which is underlain by the station and running tunnels of the Bakerloo Line, the top of the Lambeth Group is at a depth of approximately 39 m bgl. A description of the site investigation at WIT has been given by Pickles and Everton (1996) and predictions and measurements of ground movements during construction have been presented by Hight *et al* (1993).

Angel Station Reconstruction, Islington

Reconstruction of London Underground's Angel Station is described by Moriarty and Cooper (1991), with geotechnical aspects dealt with by Mair *et al* (1997). The project comprised the construction of new escalator and concourse tunnels, station tunnel and step-plate junctions, together with a length of running tunnel. The new 7.5 m ID escalator tunnel was constructed between the piled foundations of a six-storey building in London Clay. The axes of the new tunnels were close to the interface between the London Clay and the Upper Mottled Clay of the Lambeth Group. Ground level was at approximately 34 m OD, with the top of the Lambeth Group at approximately -0.7 m OD and the base at -17 m OD. Block samples of the Upper Mottled Clay were taken from the tunnel face, just below the interface with the overlying London Clay.

Sizewell Nuclear Power Station, Suffolk

Details of the recent geotechnical and geophysical investigations carried out at the Sizewell Nuclear Power Station sites on the Suffolk coast are described by Davis *et al* (1996), Hepton (1996) and Hight *et al* (1997). At these sites, the Lambeth Group exists between depths of approximately 67 m and 79 m bgl, being overlain by the Crag and London Clay and underlain by the Ormesby Clay and Chalk. It appears to be one of the few sites at which measurements of both compression and shear wave velocities have been made in the Lambeth Group.

4.2 SOURCES OF DATA FOR HAMPSHIRE BASIN

In contrast to the London Basin, there is a paucity of available data for the Hampshire Basin. Data from the following site have been obtained.

Portsmouth and Havant Waste Water Tunnel

A 7.5 km tunnel is being constructed beneath Portsmouth and Langstone Harbour to carry wastewater to a new treatment works at Havant and treated water to a new 5.7 km-long sea outfall. Because of the southerly dip of the beds, the tunnel will pass through the Chalk, the Lambeth Group, London Clay and Bracklesham Beds.

4.3 DEPOSITIONAL ENVIRONMENTS AND POST-DEPOSITIONAL PROCESSES

To assist in understanding the engineering properties of the soils that make up the different units of the Lambeth Group, Table 4.1 attempts to summarise the key points related to their:

- depositional environment
- post-depositional history, separating this into the three stages of: immediate post-depositional; burial; uplift, erosion and weathering.

(Composition, a third factor determining engineering behaviour, is dealt with in Section 4.6.)

Table 4.1   *Summary of depositional environments and post-depositional processes associated with the Lambeth Group*

Formation	Sedimentary depositional environment			Immediate post depositional	Burial	Uplift, erosion and weathering
	Primary structures due to deposition of particles and to environment of deposition			Changes due to the processes immediately after sedimentation and before deep burial	Changes due to burial at depth (where $\sigma_v' >$ 'quasi' p'_c continued reduction in void ratio)	Changes due to reduction in overburden and exposure to surface effects
Woolwich	Shallow water brackish, restricted marine/tidal estuary with storm/high energy events	Meso-structures Laminations, Cross-bedding, Bioturbation, Soft sediment deformation	Mega-structures Channel structures	Root action. Cementation. (In extreme, conversion to Reading Formation by pedogenesis)	Cementation	Faulting and discontinuities due to tectonism and reductions in stress Swelling (increases in void ratio)
Reading	Alluvial plain – overbank deposits cut by river channels possibly tidally influenced	Original structures lost due to pedogenesis. Cross-bedding in channel sand	Channel structures (sand bodies)	Pedogenesis – soil-forming processes such as formation of duricrust, cementation, desiccation, fissuring, redox reactions, burrowing by organism, root action	Cementation	Oxidation/ reduction of mineral and organic content Dissolution
Upnor (Pebble Beds)	Shallow offshore/inshore marine – high energy			Pedogenesis, duricrust formation/ cementation	Cementation	
Upnor (Glauconitic Beds)	Shallow offshore marine – shoreface (medium energy)	Cross-bedding Bioturbation	Cross-bedding	Pedogenesis – cementation, burrowing by organisms	Cementation	

4.3.1   Depositional history

As described in Chapter 2, three distinctly different depositional environments existed at the edge of the North Sea Basin in which the material of the Lambeth Group was laid down. With changes in relative sea level, these environments shifted either landward or seaward. The Upnor Formation was deposited in a shallow sea environment (< 20 m water depth) and its sedimentation was influenced by tidal flows. The deposits comprise shallow marine sands and pebbles with a variable clay/silt content, and the initial fabric included laminae and thin beds of clay within the sand. Discontinuous pebble beds occur throughout the formation.

A reduction in sea level, and possibly uplift, occurred, leading to emergence and to a terrestrial environment in which the Reading Formation (Lower Mottled Clay) was formed. Clays and silts were laid down on vegetated mudflats, forming an alluvial plain crossed by river channels, leading to the presence of sand-filled channel structures. The prevailing sub-tropical climate involved pronounced wet and dry seasons and subaerial weathering. Pedogenesis affected the sediments, including the Upnor Formation, where this was close to the ground surface.

Page (1994) refers to the Mid-Lambeth Group hiatus, corresponding to the widespread change from this terrestrial environment over the eastern part of the basin, and leading to the deposition of the Lower Shelly Clay and Laminated beds of the Woolwich Formation on the Lower Mottled Clay. The Woolwich Formation was deposited in a brackish-water lagoonal or estuarine environment, leading to interfingering sands, silts and clays. Shelly beds occur at the base of the Woolwich Formation. A second emergent phase and return to a terrestrial environment resulted in the formation of the Upper Mottled Clay, overlying the Woolwich Formation in the east. A third transgression was responsible for the formation of the Upper Shelly Clay (Woolwich Formation – upper leaf) in central and southern London.

4.3.2   Immediate post-depositional events

Not only does the Lambeth Group differ in terms of depositional environment from the London Clay, which was deposited in marine conditions, but also in the wide range of post-depositional processes to which it has been subjected, which reflect periods of uplift and emergence. Immediate post-depositional processes included bioturbation, pedogenesis and weathering. Bioturbation occurred throughout the Lambeth Group and a particularly intensively burrowed horizon corresponds to the Mid-Lambeth Group hiatus. Pedogenic processes in a sub-tropical climate affected all the formations of the Lambeth Group. These processes involved dissolution, precipitation, transport, oxidation and reduction associated with fluctuating water tables, and reduction associated with root development. The processes led to the following.

1   Mottling as the sediments were oxidised to varying degrees.

2   Clay enrichment, with clay being transported into the sands, and clay coatings developing on sand grains and pebbles.

3   Changes in mineralogy.

4   Destruction of shells by dissolution and removal of organics by oxidation.

5   Cementing, involving a variety of processes, including the formation of duricrusts/ pedocretes and the precipitation of cements. The form of cement would have depended on the local permeability and proximity of sources of cementing agents: thus, carbonate is present as a pervasive cement throughout the sands and gravels in London, forming weakly cemented gravel, limestone (particularly in the vicinity of the shell beds), or calcrete, silcrete or ferricrete; in the clays, calcrete occurs as fine to medium gravel sized powdery concretions – in the sandier sediments in east London, larger nodules and more extensive carbonate cementing, up to 1 m thick, has developed in the Lower Mottled Clay. Examples of the calcretes that formed in the London area at the time of the Mid-Lambeth Group hiatus are shown in Figures 4.3 and 4.4. Figure 4.3 is a core sample from JLE borehole 404T, showing its irregular nature in clays, and Figure 4.4 an exposure at Canada Water Station on the JLE, showing the calcrete duricrust on a pebble bed, and representing a former hardpan. Occasionally, the sands contain much harder silicretes, as in north London, where silica cementation pedogenesis of the pebble beds has formed the Hertfordshire Puddingstone, and ferricretes, as at Newhaven.

6   Modification of primary sedimentary structures, eg laminations, and the introduction of fissuring. Fissuring in the mottled clays has arisen as a result of desiccation, with polishing and slickensiding thought to be the result of cyclic (seasonal) movements. Three scales of fissuring have been observed:

   (a)   at the pedological scale, involving fissures at 4 mm spacing or less. An example from the Upper Mottled Clay at Newbury is presented in Figure 4.5. The fissures are polished where the clay is of intermediate or high plasticity.

   (b)   at the 100 mm scale.

(c) at the 1000 mm scale, possibly related to desiccation and dewatering or to the effects of ground ice and likely, therefore, to be within 10 m of the surface.

Some fissuring is also evident in the clay layers within the Woolwich Formation.

There are indications that cementing may subsequently have developed across the small and medium scale fissures, as infilling of shrinkage cracks took place and as cementing agents seeped through and were precipitated on fissure surfaces.

Figure 4.3   *Calcrete in Lower Mottled Clay, JLE borehole 404T, Maltby Street, Tower Bridge Road*

Figure 4.4   *Calcrete below Lower Shelly Clay, Canada Water Station, Rotherhithe*

Figure 4.5 *Four millimetre scale fissuring in Upper Mottled Clay, Newbury Bypass*

4.3.3   Later post-depositional events

After pedogenesis, the Lambeth Group was buried beneath the full thickness of the remainder of the Palaeogene sequence, which has been eroded in part or in full, following uplift 20 million years ago. The materials are, therefore, heavily overconsolidated. No estimate of preconsolidation pressure has been made and it would be difficult because of cementing, but removal of not less than 250 m of sediments has occurred in central London. Overconsolidation ratio is likely to vary across the basins. Swelling has accompanied uplift and erosion. Both the initial burial and the subsequent swelling may have damaged cementation. This is more likely in the higher plasticity, more expansive clays. Additional fissuring may also have developed on unloading, although this will have been resisted by the presence of cementing.

Weathering is continuing where the materials are currently exposed.

Tectonic activity, associated with the rapidly subsiding North Sea Basin, has resulted in shear surfaces and minor faults throughout the Lambeth Group.

Periglacial activity led to the development of pingos, in which disturbed Lambeth Group sediments have been injected through the London Clay, and other features such as ice wedges and buried channels.

4.4   GENERALISED GEOTECHNICAL DESCRIPTIONS

Typical geotechnical descriptions of the units that make up the Lambeth Group in the London and Hampshire Basins are presented in Tables 4.2. and 4.3 respectively.

Table 4.2 *Examples of engineering descriptions (London Basin)*

Unit	Example description
Upper Shelly Clay (USC) (0–2 m)	Dark grey and grey-brown, stiff silty clay or clayey silt, locally with fine sand. Shells (including oysters) and sporadic flints. Impersistent limestone beds (towards base).
Upper Mottled Clay (UMC) (up to 7.5 m)	Mottled red-brown, brown, blue-grey, very stiff to hard, closely fissured silty clay with beds of thinly laminated silt and fine sand. Slickensided fissures are at scales of 4 mm and 100 mm. Occasional sand-filled channel structures.
Laminated beds (Lb) (up to 9 m)	Grey to dark brown, thinly interbedded silty clay, clayey silt and silty fine to medium sand. Beds are generally less than 50 mm thick and are typically finely laminated down to 1 mm scale. Occasional shells and some lignitic matter. Occasional sand-filled channel structures. Sands locally silicified.
Lower Shelly Clay (LSC) (up to 9m)	Dark grey to black, very stiff fissured clay with minor sand and silt interbeds. Shell (including oysters) layers. Locally weakly cemented limestone bands (up to 1.6 m thick) where shells are concentrated.
Lower Mottled Clay (LMC) (0–5 m)	Mottled purple, red, brown and grey green very stiff to hard, closely fissured silty clay – blocky, unbedded, with patchy cobble-size carbonate concretions up to 0.5 m in diameter (duricrusts). Weak to moderately strong argillaceous limestone as nodules and bands at irregular intervals (up to 1.3 m thick). Occasional flint gravel and sand (Lower Mottled Sand) becomes dominant east of London.
Pebble bed (pb) (0–2.5 m)	Blue-green and grey, fine to coarse gravel comprising rounded flint pebbles, both clast and matrix supported. Matrix is pale green to dark green sandy clay or sand. Upper part may have weak carbonate cement.
Glauconitic sand (GS) (3.5–6 m)	Green, grey and brown, clayey, very silty glauconitic fine to medium sand with laminae and thin clay beds (up to 300 mm) of matrix supported flint pebbles. Sometimes bioturbated. Patchily cemented by calcium carbonate into large irregular calcareous concretions.

Table 4.3 *Typical description of Lambeth Group units in the Hampshire Basin*

Formation	Western part of Basin	Eastern part of Basin
Reading	Mottled red, grey, purple and orange multi-coloured fissured clay and silty clay Channels infilled with fine to coarse sand	East of Hove – absent
Woolwich	Poorly developed west of Chichester	Laminated clays, silts and fine sands with variable organic content of lignite and shells Grey silty clay with shells
Upnor	West of Portsmouth – absent. Replaced by light grey, cross-bedded fine to coarse sand with some flint gravel of fluvial origin (Reading Formation)	Rapidly reduces in thickness west of Hove from orange, brown, limonitic, fine to coarse sand to light purple/blue and green silty mottled clayey fine sand

Note: Lambeth Group everywhere directly lies on the Chalk. A bed of coarse gravel of angular flint and chalk may lie at the base. This bed maybe cemented or weathered to clay with flints. Thickness of individual units is variable across the basin. Differentiation of the individual members is difficult and Formation names are recommended.

The composition and, therefore, the description of individual units varies. Thus, the Lower Mottled Clay becomes increasingly sandy towards the east of the London Basin and takes on the description of a sand and gravel.

As a result of their previous desiccation, the Upper and Lower Mottled Clays are described as very stiff to hard. Measured strengths may not be consistent with this description because of the influence of fissures. Clays of the Woolwich Formation are usually described as very stiff.

Typical photographs of cores and exposures of the different units that make up the Lambeth Group are presented in Appendix 2.

4.5 DISTRIBUTION

In the London Basin, the Lambeth Group attains thicknesses of 30–40 m west of London and thins towards the east because of greater erosion. Beneath London, the thickness varies between 15 m and 20 m.

To the east of London, the Reading Formation occurs as two leaves: the upper leaf, the Upper Mottled Clay, lies between the Upper Shelly Clay and Laminated beds of the Woolwich Formation; the lower leaf, the Lower Mottled Clay, lies between the Lower Shelly Clay and the Upnor Formation. This interleaving does not occur west of London.

The Reading Formation is absent in Essex and Kent.

The Lambeth Group at Newbury is quite different to that in central London in that the Woolwich Formation, ie the shelly clays and laminated beds, are absent. Instead, the Reading Formation lies directly on the Upnor Formation, which is almost entirely a green glauconitic sand with large oyster shells and little quartz. The Reading beds are all mottled and it is difficult to distinguish the Upper Mottled and Lower Mottled Clay sequences. Sand-filled river channels are frequent, becoming wider and the sands cleaner higher in the sequence. Data from the Newbury Bypass has been separated in some of the following figures into that for the clays of the Mottled Clays and the granular materials of the sand channels and Upnor Formation.

4.6 COMPOSITION

Gradings

Grading envelopes established on projects in the London Basin for the different units of the Lambeth Group are presented in Figures 4.6–4.11. These reveal the following features.

1   The particularly wide envelope for the Upper Mottled Clay, with the material varying between a clay with 80 per cent clay-size particles and a medium sand. Generally, the clay contents range between 2 and 50 per cent. The clay/silts represent overbank deposits, ie material carried in suspension during the flooding of non-migrating channels; the sands represent channel sand bodies.

2   The Lower Mottled Clay, generally falling into one of two envelopes, with the coarser envelope representing the more sandy succession in the east of the London Basin; occasionally, gradings span between the two envelopes.

3   The Laminated beds also falling into one of two envelopes; almost inevitably mixing of clay and silt or sand laminae has occurred prior to grading, modifying both grading envelopes. It is reported that Laminated beds change from predominantly clays with I_p greater than 40 per cent in the west to silty fine to medium sands with lower-plasticity clays ($I_p < 25$ per cent) in the east.

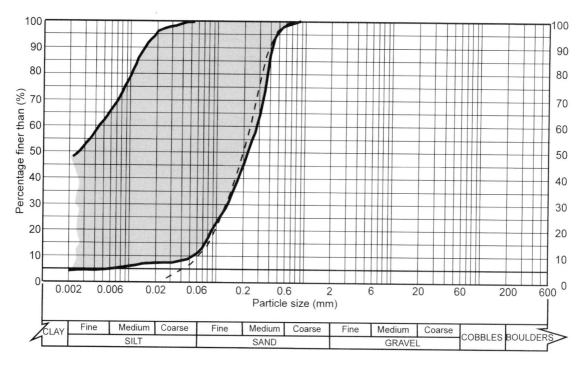

Figure 4.6   *Grading envelope for Upper Mottled Clay (Reading Formation). JLE: Green Park to Canada Water*

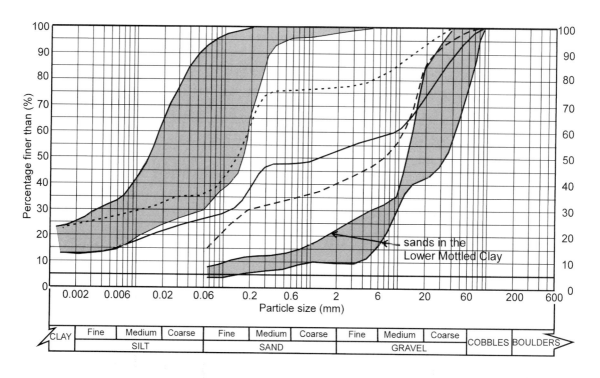

Figure 4.7   *Grading envelope for Lower Mottled Clay (Reading Formation). JLE: Green Park to Canada Water and Canada Water to Pioneer Wharf*

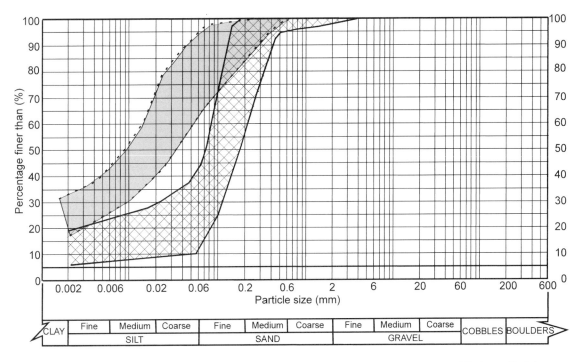

Figure 4.8   *Grading envelope for Laminated beds (Woolwich Formation). JLE: Green Park to Canada Water, Canada Water to Pioneer Wharf and Limmo Site to Stratford Station*

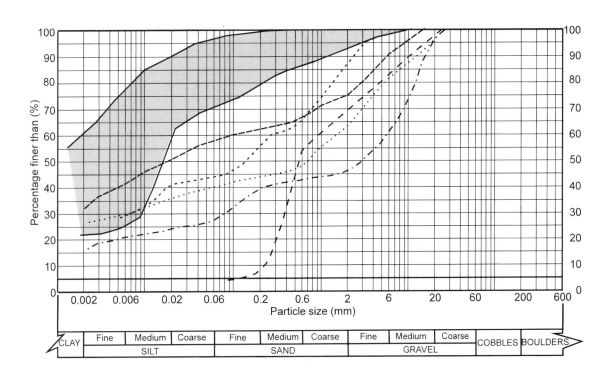

Figure 4.9   *Grading envelope for Lower Shelly Clay (Woolwich Formation). JLE: Green Park to Canada Water, Canada Water to Pioneer Wharf and Limmo Site to Stratford Station*

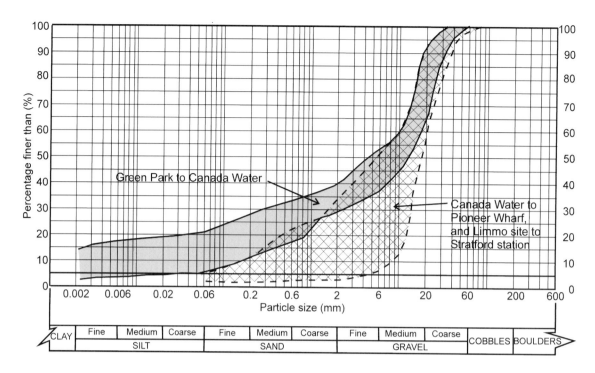

Figure 4.10 *Grading envelope for pebble beds (Upnor Formation). JLE: Green Park to Canada Water, Canada Water to Pioneer Wharf and Limmo Site to Stratford Station*

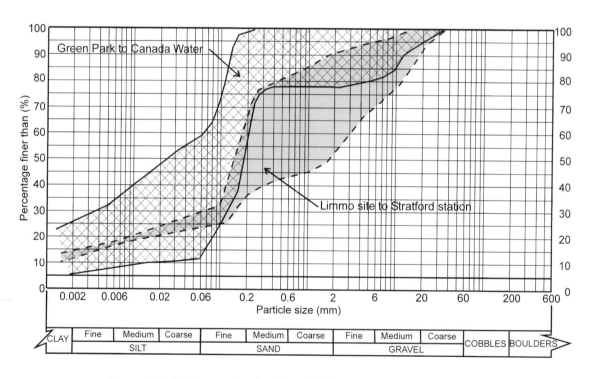

Figure 4.11 *Grading envelope for Glauconitic Sand (Upnor Formation). JLE: Green Park to Canada Water and Limmo Site to Stratford Station*

4.7   SOIL PLASTICITY

Data on the range in plasticity index, I_p, found for the clays in each unit on the Crossrail, JLE and CTRL projects is presented in Figures 4.12 and 4.13. The predominant values are as follows:

Lambeth group unit	I_p (per cent)
Upper Mottled Clay	25–45
Laminated beds	15–35
Lower Shelly Clay	25–35
Lower Mottled Clay	20–35
Upnor Formation	15–30

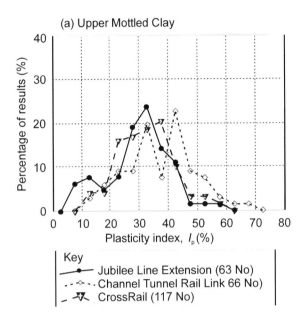

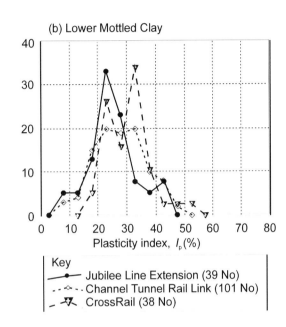

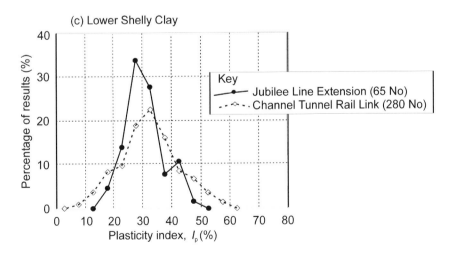

Figure 4.12   *Ranges of plasticity index, I_p, in Upper Mottled Clay, Lower Mottled Clay and Lower Shelly Clay. JLE, CTRL and Crossrail*

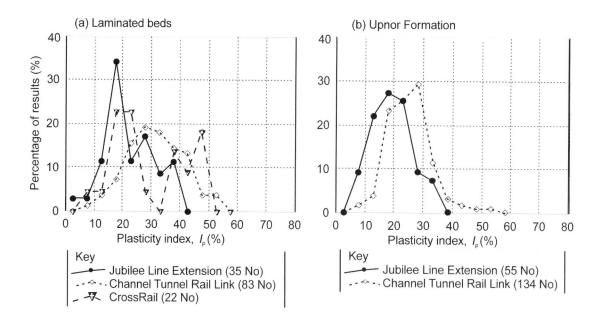

Figure 4.13 *Ranges of plasticity index, I_p, in Laminated beds and Upnor Formation. JLE, CTRL and Crossrail*

There is a relatively wide range for I_p in each unit. Clays in the Upper Mottled Clay are generally more plastic than the other clays and show a tendency to reduce in plasticity towards the east. The narrowest range of plasticity is in the Lower Shelly Clay and the lowest plasticities are found in the clays of the Upnor Formation. Data for the Laminated beds from Crossrail show two peaks for I_p, between 15 and 25 per cent and between 35 and 50 per cent. In several of the units I_p straddles the value of 25 per cent, the engineering significance of which is discussed in Section 4.13.

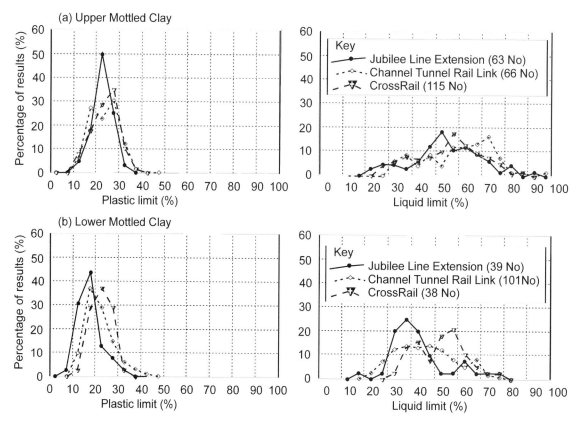

Figure 4.14 *Distribution of plastic and liquid limits in Upper Mottled and Lower Mottled Clays*

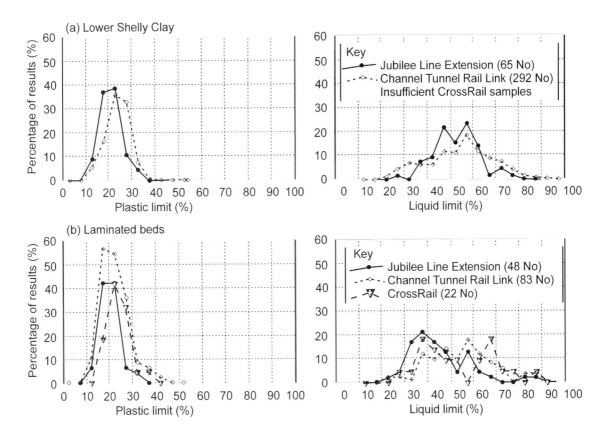

Figure 4.15 *Distribution of plastic and liquid limits in Lower Shelly Clay and Laminated beds*

In Figures 4.14 to 4.16, distributions of liquid limit, w_L, and plastic limit w_p, are shown for the different units. These illustrate that more of the variability is in w_L.

Variations in I_p with depth on the various projects in London are shown in Figures 4.17 and 4.18, with the different units being distinguished. Data for Crossrail, JLE, CTRL London Tunnels East and West are representative of the variations in I_p on a project basis; data for Farringdon Station and CTRL Stratford Box are representative of the variations at a single site. Data on plasticity index of the Mottled Beds versus depth on the Newbury Bypass are presented in Figure 4.19.

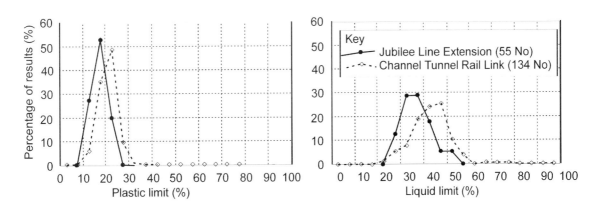

Figure 4.16 *Distribution of plastic and liquid limits in Upnor Formation*

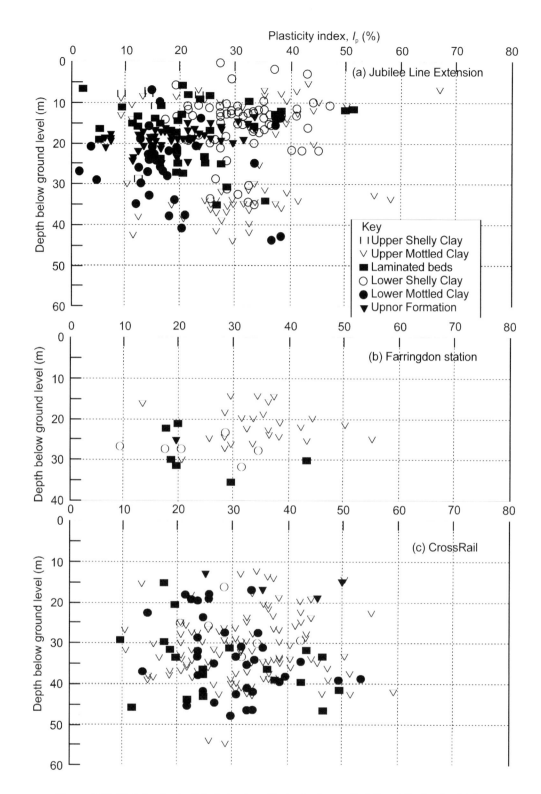

Figure 4.17 *Variation in plasticity index, I_p, with depth. Crossrail, JLE and Farringdon Station*

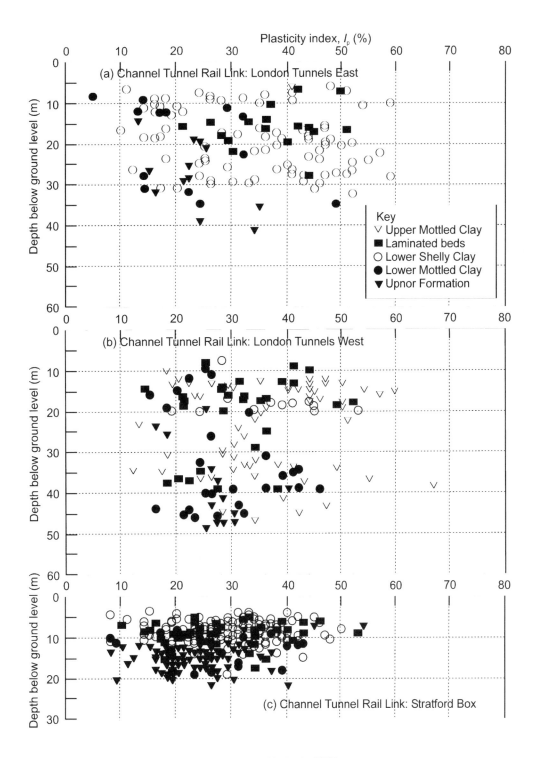

Figure 4.18 *Variation in plasticity index, I_p, with depth, CTRL*

It is immediately apparent that the variation in I_p at a single site is similar to that over the whole project. There is clearly no pattern to the variations when examined in terms of depth below ground level. Plots of I_p versus height above the base of a unit (eg Figure 4.20) show a slight trend for I_p to increase towards the base of the unit in the case of the Upper and Lower Mottled Clay and the Laminated beds.

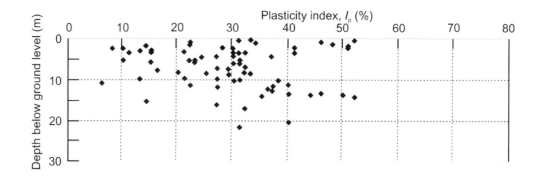

Figure 4.19 *Variation in plasticity index, I$_p$, with depth. Mottled Clay, Newbury Bypass*

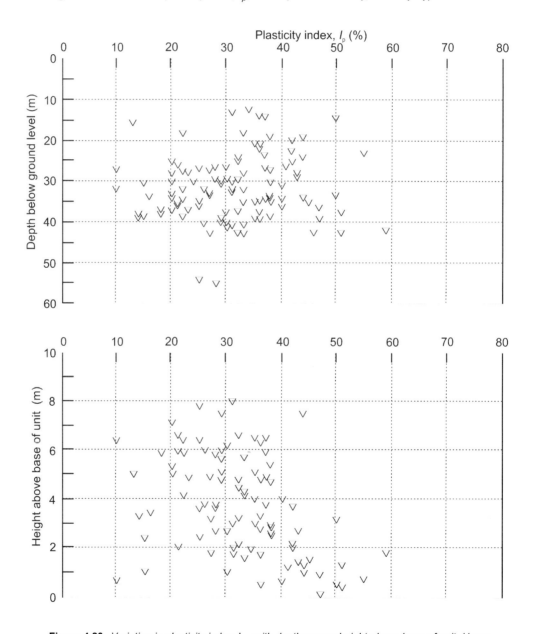

Figure 4.20 *Variation in plasticity index, I$_p$, with depth versus height above base of unit. Upper Mottled Clay, Crossrail*

Similarly, there are no strong trends in the data for each unit, from west to east, along the JLE and CTRL London Tunnels and Stratford Box, see Figures 4.12 and 4.22. However, these figures do reflect the change in stratigraphy across London, for example:

- along the CTRL (Figure 4.22), the Upper Mottled Clay predominate at the western end, where the Lambeth Group is overlain by the London Clay. At the Stratford Box and to the east, the upper units have been removed by erosion and the Lower Shelly Clay are now the predominant cohesive unit

- similarly, along the line of the JLE (Figure 4.21), the Upper Mottled Clay predominate to the west, but do not appear east of Canada Water.

Despite these changes in stratigraphy, a similar level of variability in I_p persists, although possibly reducing, together with maximum I_p, towards the east. Again, note how I_p data falls above and below the value of 25 per cent.

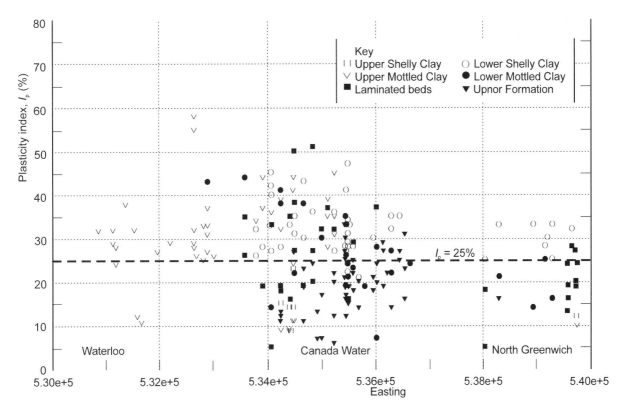

Figure 4.21 *Plasticity index in Lambeth Group from west to east along Jubilee Line Extension*

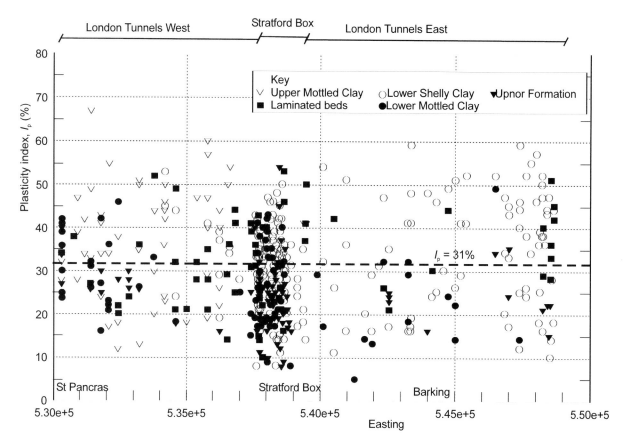

Figure 4.22 *Plasticity index in Lambeth Group from west to east along CTRL, London Tunnels*

I_p data can be expected, therefore, to vary both vertically and laterally. The contrast between I_p for the London Clay and the Lambeth Group also varies. Figure 4.23 compares profiles of w_L, w_p and w_o through the London Clay and the upper part of the Lambeth Group at Waterloo International Terminal (WIT) and at Angel Station, Islington. Figure 4.24 makes a similar comparison at Farringdon Station. At WIT and Farringdon Station there is a major reduction in plasticity close to the boundary between the London Clay and Upper Mottled Clay, which begins towards the base of the London Clay. At Angel Station the Upper Mottled Clay are of similar plasticity to the London Clay and reductions in plasticity only occur below -8m OD.

CIRIA C583

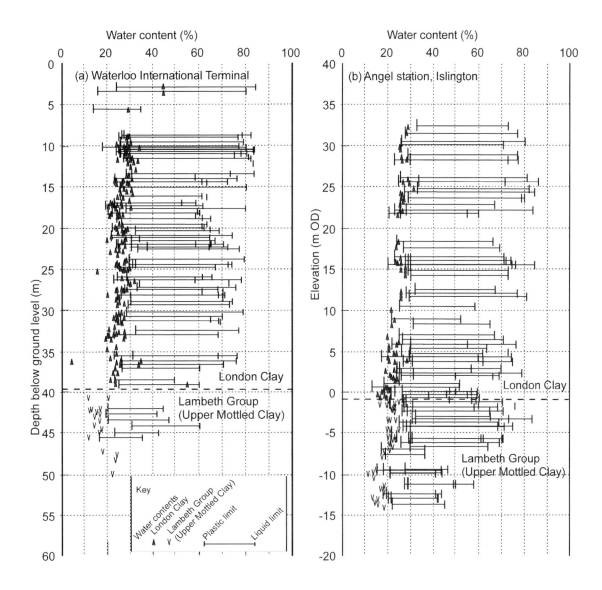

Figure 4.23 *Contrast between index properties in London Clay and Upper Mottled Clay at (a) Waterloo International Terminal and (b) Angel Station, Islington*

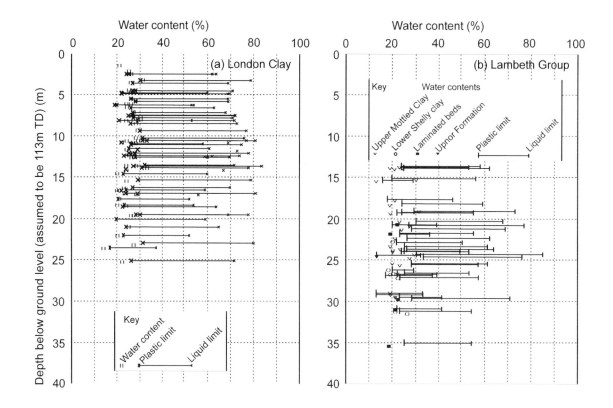

Figure 4.24 *Contrast between index properties in London Clay and Lambeth Group at Farringdon Station*

Casagrande plots for the different units in the London area are presented in Figures 4.25 and 4.26. Almost all the data plots above the A line, with no obvious differences between the units.

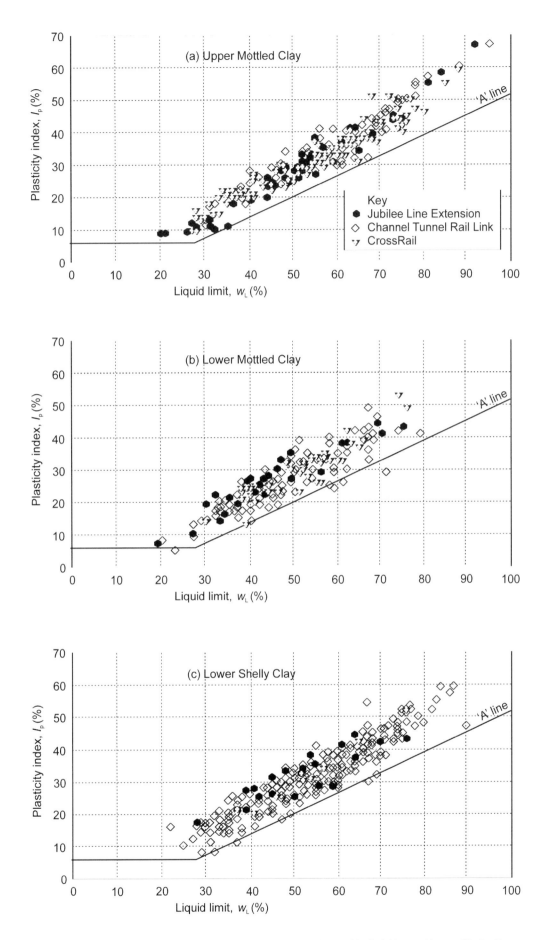

Figure 4.25 *Casagrande plots for Upper Mottled Clay, Lower Mottled Clay and Lower Shelly Clay. JLE, CTRL and Crossrail*

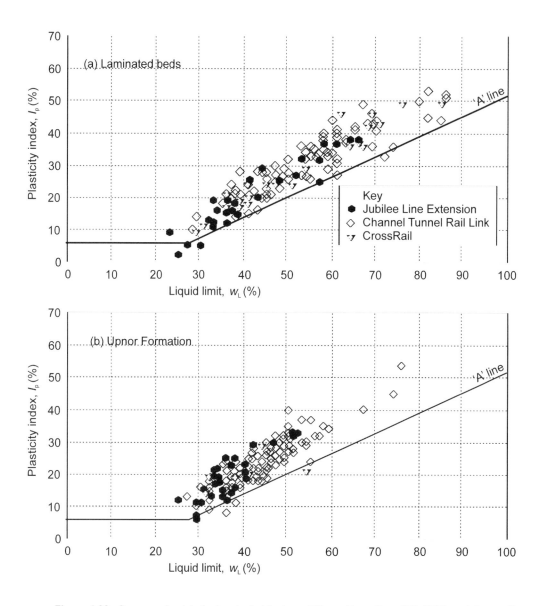

Figure 4.26 *Casagrande plots for Laminated beds and Upnor Formation. JLE, CTRL and Crossrail*

4.8   CLAY MINERALOGY

As a result of volcanic activity in Scotland and Iceland at the time of deposition, smectite tends to be the dominant clay mineral in the Upnor Formation, except where it has undergone pedogenesis and where illite becomes dominant, with kaolinite also present. Similar combinations of smectite, illite and kaolinite are found in the pedogenesised Lower and Upper Mottled Clay. The Lower Shelly Clay is rich in kaolinite but may contain layers of ash. Ash layers are also present in the Upnor Formation.

4.9   LIQUIDITY INDEX

Variations in liquidity index, I_L, with depth on the various projects in London are shown in Figures 4.27 and 4.28, with the different units being distinguished. While most of the data from Crossrail falls below zero, which would be expected in heavily overconsolidated clays, there is a surprisingly large amount of data showing I_L greater than zero on JLE and CTRL, with a particularly wide scatter on each project.

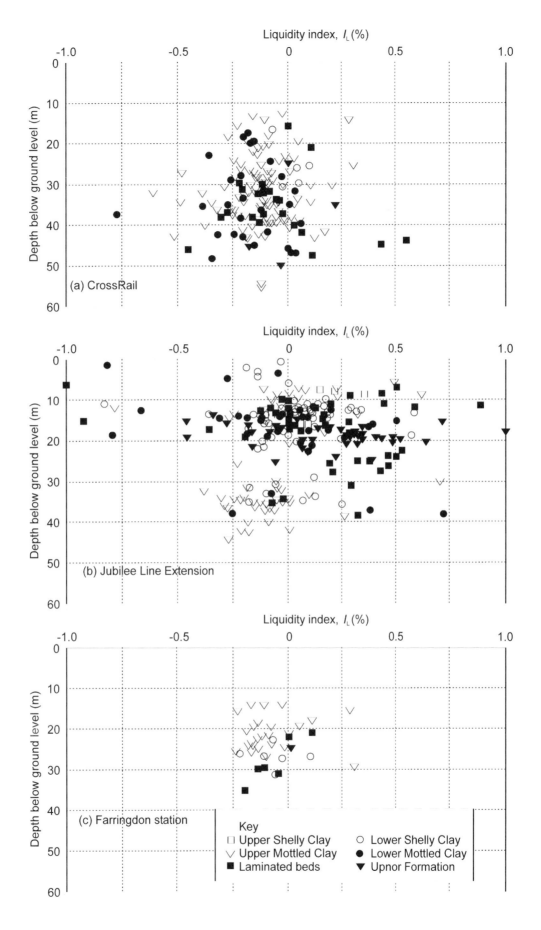

Figure 4.27 *Variation in liquidity index, I*$_L$*, with depth. Crossrail, JLE and Farringdon Station*

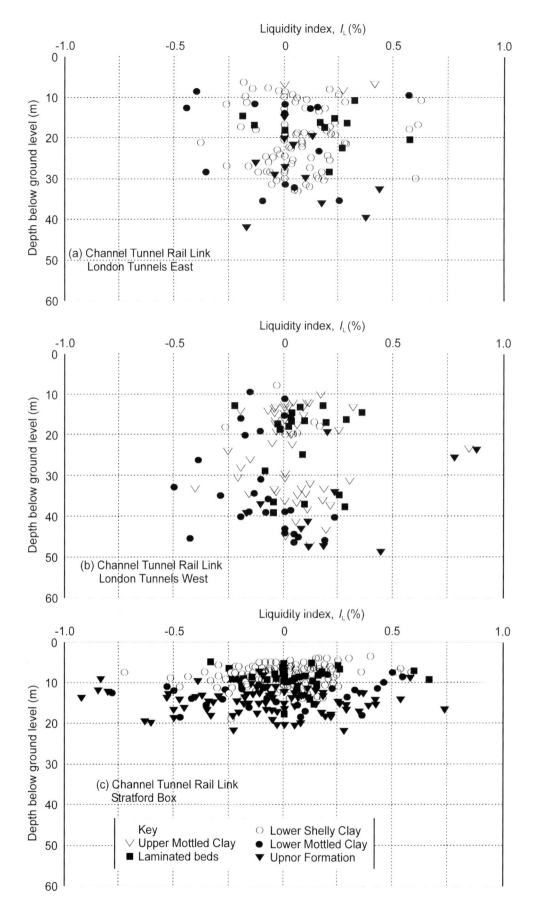

Figure 4.28 *Variation in liquidity index, I_L, with depth, CTRL*

Some increase in I_L would be expected in the units that are close to the ground surface, as a result of swelling to relatively low effective stresses. However, high values of I_L are recorded, even at depth, on each project. In many cases, the high values of I_L were measured on material from the Laminated beds, the Upper and Lower Shelly Clays and the Upnor Formation. These high values of I_L and the particularly low values, are probably spurious, and result either from the mixing of sands and clays in these predominantly laminated or layered units, or from the redistribution of water in these units on release of total stress, as discussed in Section 6.6. Also discussed in Section 6.6 is the fact that high I_L values tend to be measured on tube samples, rather than rotary cored samples.

If it is assumed that the extreme scatter in I_L, for values of I_p less than 30 per cent, is due to the effects of sampling and testing, then the range of values of I_L where I_p exceeds 30 per cent may be more representative of *in situ* conditions and these are summarised below.

Project	Units	Range of values of I_L (for $I_p \geq 30\%$)
Crossrail	UMC, Lb, LMC	-0.3 → +0.05
CTRL	UMC, LSC, Lb, LMC	-0.3 → +0.3
JLE	UMC, LSC, Lb, LMC	-0.3 → +0.3

The variation in liquidity index with depth in the Mottled Clay at Newbury Bypass is shown in Figure 4.29. The higher values here probably reflect swelling after unloading at these shallow depths.

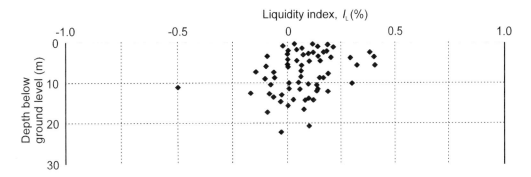

Figure 4.29 *Variation in liquidity index, I_L, with depth. Mottled Clay, Newbury Bypass*

4.10   BULK DENSITY

Variations in bulk density with depth are plotted for the different projects in London in Figures 4.30 and 4.31. The data for CTRL, which are rather limited, have been combined into one plot. The range for each project is remarkably similar and the variability at a single site (Farringdon Station) is similar to the variability over the whole project (Crossrail).

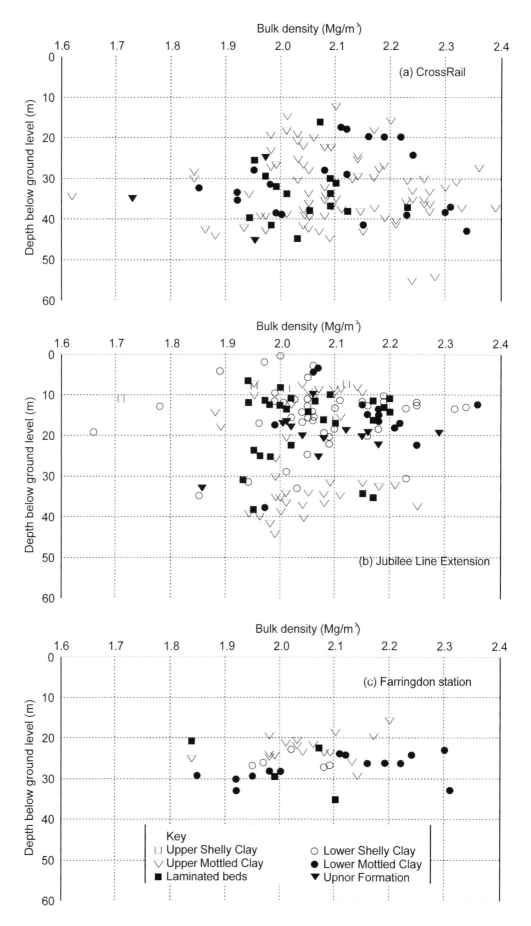

Figure 4.30 *Variation in bulk density with depth. Crossrail, JLE and Farringdon Station*

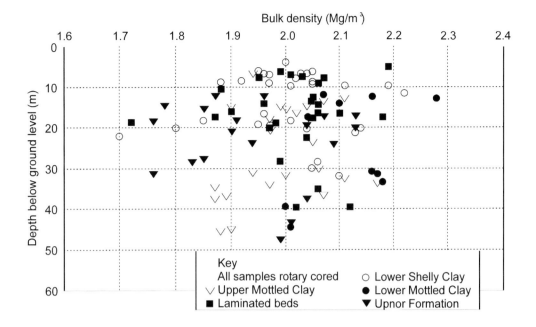

Figure 4.31 *Variation in bulk density with depth. CTRL: London Tunnels and Stratford Box*

While the range of measured values for bulk density reflects in part a real variation in *in situ* density, resulting from different levels of cementing and desiccation, the presence or not of duricrusts or limestone layers etc, some of the variability is almost certainly induced by sampling effects. Thus, for example, low values often relate to samples from the Upnor Formation, Lower Shelly Clay and Laminated beds, which have desaturated on stress relief. In addition, much of the data have been obtained from driven tube samples, which can cause fracturing in hard clays and a reduction in density, as discussed in Section 6.6. Values of bulk density less than approximately 1.95 Mg/m³ in the Lambeth Group below central London should be treated with caution.

There can be a marked contrast in bulk density on passing from the London Clay into the Upper Mottled Clay. Examples for WIT and Farringdon Station are presented in Figures 4.32 and 4.33.

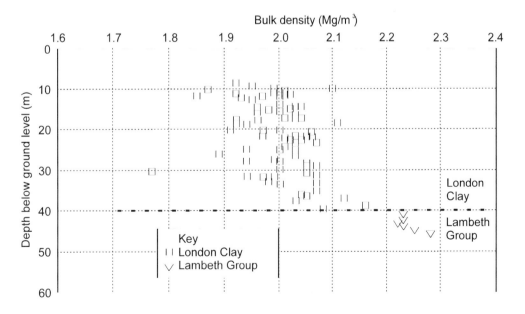

Figure 4.32 *Contrast between bulk density in London Clay and Upper Mottled Clay at Waterloo International Terminal*

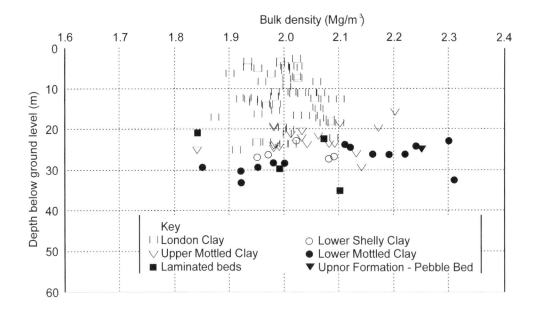

Figure 4.33 *Contrast between bulk density in London Clay and Lambeth Group at Farringdon Station*

The variation in bulk density with depth in the Mottled Clay at Newbury Bypass is shown in Figure 4.34. The high values seen at depth in London are not found at these shallower depths.

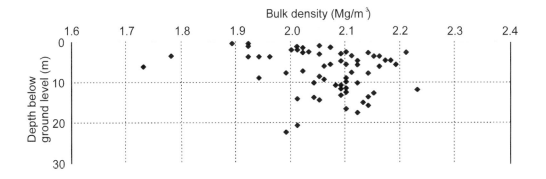

Figure 4.34 *Variation in bulk density with depth. Mottled Clay, Newbury Bypass*

4.11 GROUNDWATER CONDITIONS AND *IN-SITU* HORIZONTAL STRESSES

4.11.1 Groundwater conditions

The Lambeth Group consists of an interbedded sequence of aquifers, aquitards and aquicludes. The Upper Mottled Clay usually forms an aquiclude and the Upnor Formation forms part of the aquifer comprising the Thanet Sands and Chalk.

Groundwater conditions in the Lambeth Group in the London area are strongly influenced by the effects of under-drainage to the underlying Chalk and Thanet Sands, from which water has been extracted in the past. As such, they will be influenced in the future by the ongoing rise in groundwater levels in these strata now that water extraction has virtually ceased (Simpson *et al*, 1989). Some typical groundwater conditions that have been reported are described below.

Jubilee Line Extension

Linney and Page (1996) report that, in the area of south London traversed by the JLE, the piezometric surface in the lower aquifer, comprising the granular sub-units of the Lambeth Group and the Thanet Sands, varied between -1 m OD and -10 m OD at the time of the investigations (1990/91). For the design of the underground structures, a long-term piezometric surface of +2.5 m OD was adopted.

Crossrail

At the time of the site investigations (1992), the Laminated beds were found to be dry between Red Lion Street to Farringdon Road and the lower part of the glauconitic sands of the Upnor Formation were found to be dry at Liverpool Street Station. Typical piezometric profiles interpreted for Farringdon and Liverpool Street Stations are shown in Figure 4.35.

CTRL

At the western end of the London Tunnels Section of CTRL, the water table in the lower aquifer, ie in the Chalk, Thanet Sands and sand units of the Lambeth Group, was below the base of the London Clay at the time of the site investigation. Pore pressures in the London Clay, and probably in the upper clay units of the Lambeth Group, were depressed below hydrostatic, to approximately 70 per cent of hydrostatic, because of the underdrainage. Towards the eastern end of the tunnels, the pressures were hydrostatic in both the lower and upper (terrace gravels) aquifers.

Angel Station

At Angel Station, pore pressures measured at the interface between the London Clay and Upper Mottled Clay (-2 m OD) at the time of the site investigation were about 50 per cent of the hydrostatic values corresponding to a groundwater level at +27 m OD, as a result of underdrainage.

Limehouse Link

Generally, groundwater was encountered at 5 m below ground level and was hydrostatic to a depth of about 15 m at the time of the site investigation, below which the piezometric elevation had been lowered by underdrainage to the Chalk.

4.11.2 *In-situ* horizontal stresses

On the basis of their recent stress history and heavy overconsolidation, K_o values in the clay units of the Lambeth Group would be expected to be greater than unity and to increase towards the top of the formation. Significant variability is likely because of the variations in plasticity, cementing and desiccation.

Estimates of K_o have been made in some of the projects in London on the basis of lift off pressures in self-boring pressuremeter tests and of initial effective stresses in triaxial samples. On Crossrail, where the Lambeth Group is overlain by 10–30 m of London Clay, K_o was found to reduce from just over 2 at the top of the formation towards unity at the base. A similar range in K_o was estimated for JLE with K_o of 1.5 representing a reasonable average. At Limehouse Link, De Moor and Stevenson (1996) report K_o values of between 2.0 and 2.5. Values quoted for clay units in the Lambeth Group at British Library are 1.7 to 2.5. Values for K_o in the sand units have generally been assumed to be unity.

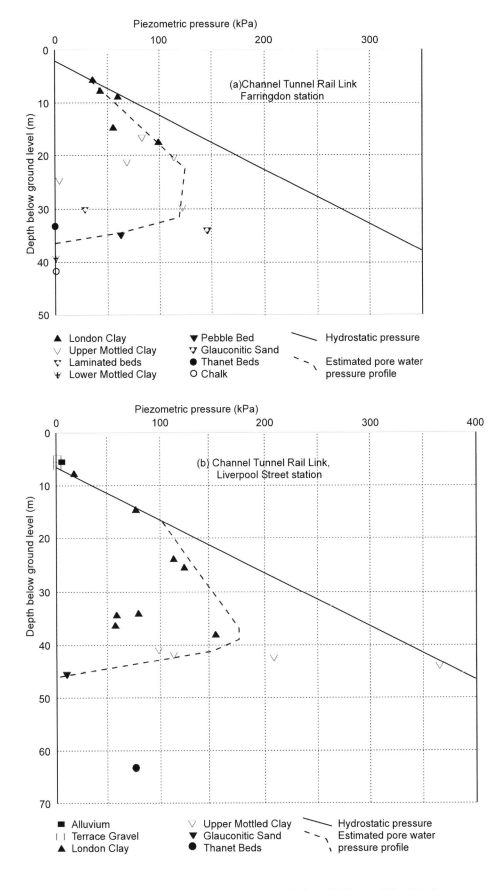

Figure 4.35 *Piezometric profiles, CTRL: (a) Farringdon Station, (b) Liverpool Street Station*

4.12 UNDRAINED STRENGTH

4.12.1 UU triaxial compression on U100 samples of clay

Some typical plots of undrained strength in clays of the Lambeth Group versus depth below ground level are presented in Figures 4.36 to 4.38. The plotted undrained strengths have been measured in unconsolidated undrained (UU) triaxial compression tests on 100 mm-diameter specimens taken from U100 samples, and represent, therefore, a conventional measurement of undrained strength. Data from Crossrail, including Farringdon Station, are representative of sites in central London where the Lambeth Group is overlain by a substantial thickness of London Clay. Data from Limehouse Link are representative of sites having a shallower cover of London Clay, in this case approximately 10 m. Data from CTRL, from West Ham Station to Stratford Station on the JLE and from Newbury Bypass are representative of sites where the top of the Lambeth Group is close to the ground surface (less than 5 m below).

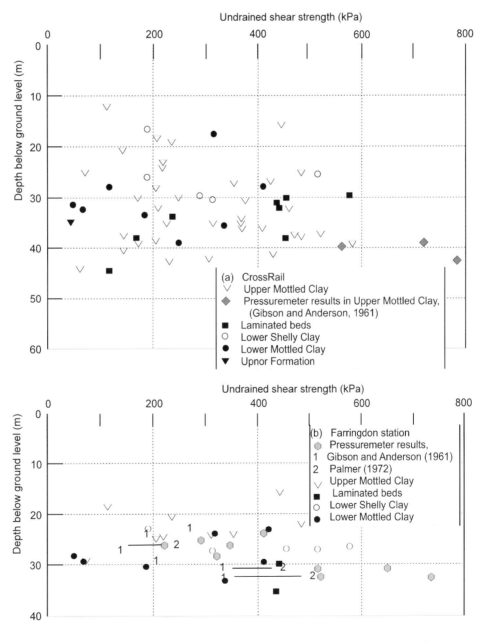

Figure 4.36 *Variation in undrained shear strength with depth. Crossrail and Farringdon Station (UU triaxial compression tests on U100 samples and pressuremeter tests)*

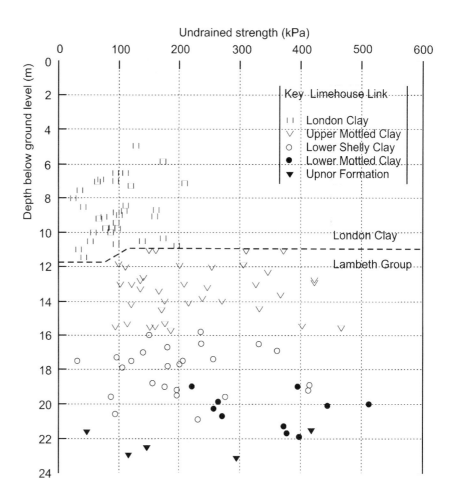

Figure 4.37 *Variation in undrained shear strength with depth. Limehouse Link (UU triaxial compression tests on U100 samples at $d\varepsilon_a/dt$ = 2 per cent/minute)*

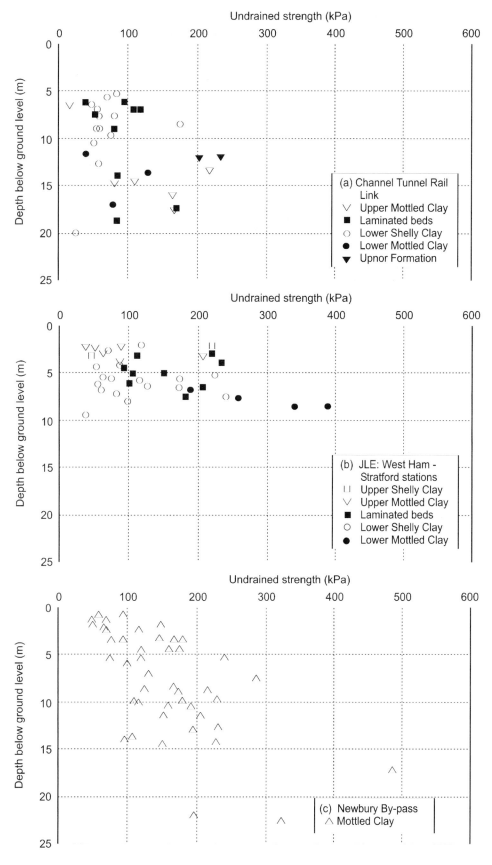

Figure 4.38 *Variation in undrained shear strength with depth. CTRL, JLE West Ham to Stratford and Newbury Bypass (UU triaxial compression tests on U100 samples)*

These plots illustrate the following, in terms of the conventional measurement of undrained strength.

1   There is a vast range in strengths at sites where the Lambeth Group is deeply buried. This mirrors the variability seen in SPT results (Section 4.15) and presumably reflects, in part at least, variations in degrees of desiccation and cementing. Undrained strengths in excess of 500 kPa were probably measured on samples with duricrust or other strong cements. The strengths, particularly in the cemented materials, are, of course, affected by sample disturbance, as discussed below.

2   At such depths, the project-wide level of variability in undrained strength, eg Crossrail, is similar to that at a single location, eg Farringdon Station (see Figure 4.36). The variability occurs in all units.

3   The strengths can be much higher than those measured in the overlying London Clay (see Figures 4.37 and 4.39, which show data from UU tests on U100 samples from both London Clay and the Lambeth Group), again reflecting the differences in depositional environments and post-depositional processes to which the Lambeth Group and London Clay have each been subjected. The lower bound to undrained strength in the Lambeth Group is more or less a continuation of the lower bound to London Clay strengths.

4   As the depth of burial reduces, there are strong indications that the undrained strengths, and their range, reduce (cf Figure 4.38 with Figures 4.36 and 4.37). This suggests that damage to structure is occurring as a result of swelling to low effective stresses.

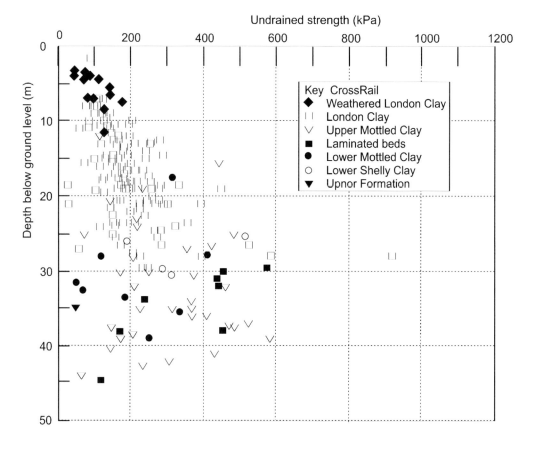

Figure 4.39 *Variation in undrained shear strength with depth in London Clay and Lambeth Group. Crossrail (UU triaxial compression tests on U100 samples)*

4.12.2   Natural versus induced variability in undrained strength

Effects of soil plasticity

It is necessary to consider the cause of this variability in undrained strength and to determine how much is natural and how much has been induced by sampling and the method of testing. Consider first the effect of differences in soil plasticity within each unit on strength in general. In Section 4.7, it was pointed out that the I_p of several units in the Lambeth Group straddles the value of 25 per cent. Two key features of soil behaviour change as I_p increases beyond 25–30 per cent in clays of these typical mineralogies. While peak angles of shearing resistance, $\varphi_p{'}$, usually show a gradual reduction with increasing plasticity, residual angles of shearing resistance, $\varphi_r{'}$, show an abrupt drop as I_p increases beyond 25–30 per cent (Figure 4.40). Low-plasticity clays undergo turbulent shear at large strains, and $\varphi_r{'}$ remains close to $\varphi_p{'}$; any brittleness in low-plasticity soils is the result of cementing or density; polishing (alignment of clay) does not occur on shear surfaces. High-plasticity clays undergo sliding shear at large strains; clay alignment (polishing) occurs on shear surfaces and $\varphi_r{'}$ drops to low residual values, well below $\varphi_p{'}$. Low-strength residual surfaces are possible in the high-plasticity clays, but unlikely in the low-plasticity clays, unless higher-plasticity clay has lodged on these surfaces.

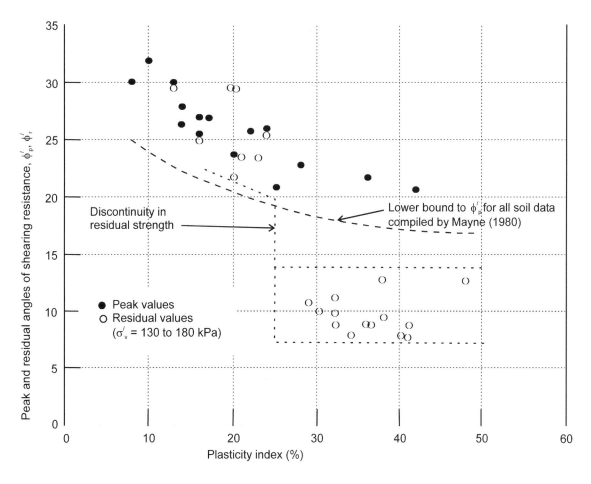

Figure 4.40 *Dependence of peak and residual angles of shearing resistance, $\varphi_p{'}$ and $\varphi_r{'}$, on soil plasticity*

The second linked feature of behaviour that changes with plasticity concerns the ability of the uncemented soil to dilate when sheared, without bifurcation, ie without a lower-strength shear zone forming. Thus, uncemented clays of low plasticity are, if sufficiently dense or overconsolidated, able to dilate to reach their ultimate or critical state strength; in undrained shear, their effective stress path climbs up the failure envelope (Figure 4.41(a)). In these clays, ultimate undrained strength is a function of water content. In contrast, overconsolidated plastic clays tend to bifurcate when reaching their peak failure envelope; a shear zone forms in which subsequent straining is concentrated and in which there is a drop from φ_p' towards φ_r'. These clays often contain lower-strength fissures, which may initiate the formation of the shear zone. In undrained shear of overconsolidated plastic clays, the effective stress path rises to reach the peak failure envelope before descending towards the post-rupture failure envelope, on its descent towards a residual state (Figure 4.41(b)). In these clays, peak undrained strength is related to the initial effective stress in the sample, p_i'.

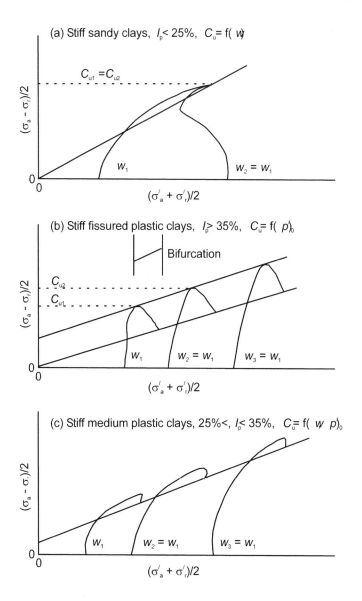

Figure 4.41 *Classification of stiff clay behaviour in undrained shear on basis of soil plasticity*

There is, almost inevitably, a group of soils of intermediate plasticity, say 25–35 per cent, which show a pattern of behaviour in undrained shear that is intermediate between that of low- and high-plasticity clays (Figure 4.41(c)). These clays show an initial capacity to dilate before there is bifurcation.

Both plasticity-dependent features of shear behaviour described above have been shown to apply to the clays of the Lambeth Group. Data on residual strength in clays from the Lambeth Group have been presented by Lehane *et al* (1995) and are discussed in Section 4.13. The strong dependence of φ_r' on I_p and the abrupt drop in φ_r' beyond I_p of

25 per cent are confirmed. Undrained triaxial compression tests on samples from Limehouse Link were carried out with the measurement of pore pressure, allowing the full effective stress paths to be defined. Typical examples are presented in Figure 4.42, separating data for low-plasticity clays from the Lower Mottled Clay and Upnor Formation and data for high-plasticity clays (I_p > 35 per cent) from the Upper Mottled Clay. These effective stress paths conform approximately to the pattern shown in Figure 4.41, suggesting that, with the range of plasticity present in the Lambeth Group, all three categories of undrained shear behaviour shown in Figure 4.41 are likely to be encountered.

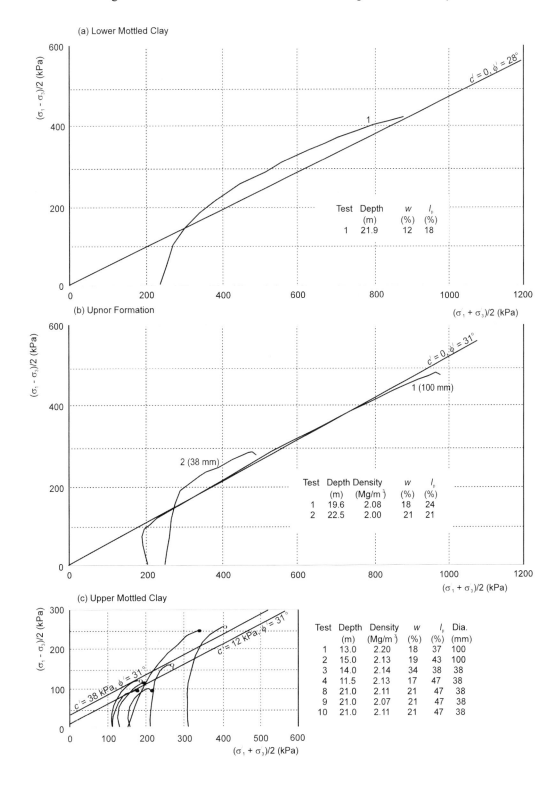

Figure 4.42 *Effective stress paths in undrained triaxial compression of low- (Lower Mottled Clay and Upnor Formation) and high- (Upper Mottled Clay) plasticity clays, Limehouse Link*

Significant differences in undrained strength can be expected, therefore, between uncemented overconsolidated clays of high and low plasticity which have experienced the same stress history. Low-plasticity clays will tend to exhibit higher undrained strengths, being able to mobilise their full ultimate strength by dilation without bifurcation. These same clays will be far more sensitive to small changes in water content, which may be natural or may occur as a result of sampling, and may well also exhibit a wider range of strengths. In high-plasticity clays, the mobilisation of high undrained strengths will be curtailed by bifurcation. Variability in strength in UU tests on these plastic clays will result from, *inter alia*, variations in initial mean effective stress in the samples.

This dependency of undrained strength on plasticity is confirmed in Figures 4.43 to 4.45, in which the data from UU triaxial compression tests from Limehouse Link, Crossrail and CTRL, have been separated into clays of high plasticity ($I_p > 35\%$), low plasticity ($I_p \leq 25\%$) and intermediate plasticity ($25\% < I_p \leq 35\%$). Clays of low plasticity generally show both the highest strengths and the higher range of strengths. (The effects of different plasticity do not apply to the London Clay, which is all of high plasticity, except towards the base of the formation.)

The discussion above considers uncemented clays and considers only the effect of soil plasticity. The picture in Figures 4.43 to 4.45 may well have been complicated by the effects of cementing and fissuring, which are now considered, and by the effects of sampling.

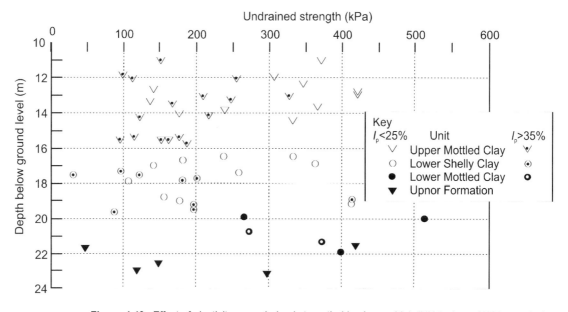

Figure 4.43 *Effect of plasticity on undrained strength. Limehouse Link (UU tests on U100 samples)*

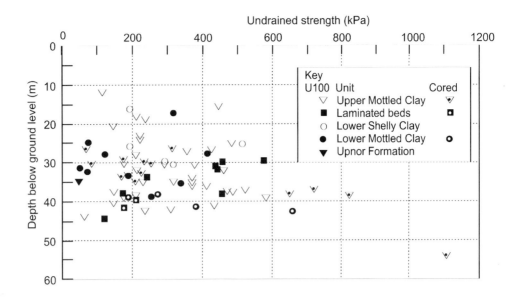

Figure 4.44 *Effect of plasticity on undrained strength. Crossrail (UU tests on U100 and cored samples)*

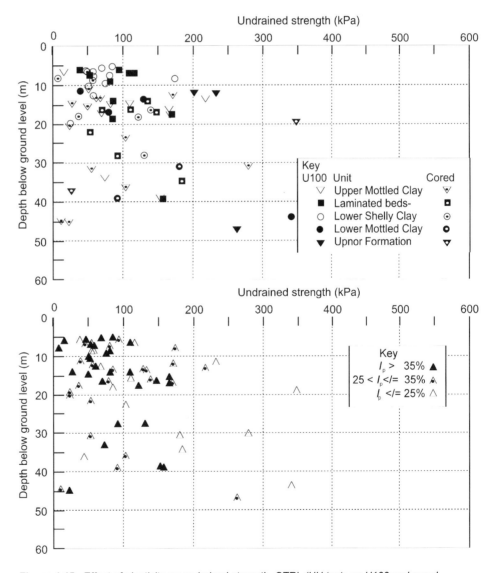

Figure 4.45 *Effect of plasticity on undrained strength. CTRL (UU tests on U100 and cored samples)*

Effects of cementing and fissuring

The different depositional environments and post-depositional processes to which the clays of the Lambeth Group have been subjected means that:

- the clays of the Reading Formation are likely to be fissured as a result of desiccation (ie shrinkage cracks) before burial

- the clays of both the Reading and Woolwich Formation are likely to be cemented to varying degrees.

In high-plasticity clays of the Reading Formation, the fissure surfaces will be polished to some extent, because of the movement on them caused by seasonal wetting and drying. In clays of low plasticity, fissure surfaces will not polish as a result of movement, as described above. Shrinkage cracking is also likely to have been less intense because of the smaller volume changes occurring in the low-plasticity material. In both cases, desiccation fissures may be cemented, having formed at an early stage in the history and provided preferred paths for percolating water.

The simplified effects of cementing on the patterns of behaviour in undrained shear of fissured and non-fissured high- and low-plasticity clays are illustrated in Figure 4.46. Cementing can overwrite the effects of plasticity described above, by introducing an additional component of strength. Similarly, cementing of even polished fissures can overwrite their effects, if the cementing is stronger than the frictional strength at the current stress state ($c' > \sigma'_n \tan \varphi'$). Thus, high strengths are possible in cemented fissured clays of both high and low plasticity.

Evidence for very high undrained strengths ($C_u > 500$ kPa) in fissured low-plasticity clays of the Lambeth Group below central London and for the existence of cementing in these clays is available from measurements in UU and CIU triaxial compression tests.

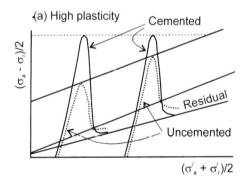

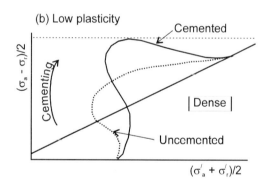

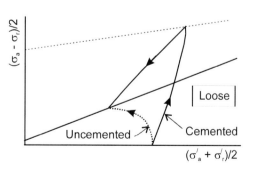

Figure 4.46 *Simplified effects of cementing on behaviour in undrained shear of fissured and non-fissured high- and low-plasticity clays*

4 Thin-wall tube samples (100 mm diameter) from the Upper and Lower Mottled Clays taken on the JLE (Ewer Street to Canada Water), which were isotropically reconsolidated and gave the following:

Unit	Depth below ground level (m)	undrained strength (kPa)	I_p (%)
UMC	10.5	-117	11
LMC	18.7	-112	37

These strengths compare to values of 120–150 kPa in UU triaxial compression tests.

In general, compression strengths are higher than extension strengths. The differences appear to increase with increasing strength (and reducing plasticity). The comparisons may, in some cases, be affected by sampling disturbance, which is likely to have reduced compression strengths more than extension strengths.

4.12.4   Undrained strength of sand units

The only test data of which the authors are aware on the strength of the sand units of the Lambeth Group is from the ground investigation at Sizewell (Davis *et al*, 1996, and Hight *et al*, 1997). In this investigation, CIU triaxial compression and extension tests were run on rotary core samples of sands, from depths between 65.3 m and 72.45 m bgl. The results are presented in Figure 4.51 and emphasise the very significant anisotropy in the material. In triaxial compression, the two measured undrained shear strengths were 593 kPa and 443 kPa; in triaxial extension, the equivalent strength was 214 kPa. Peak angles of shearing resistance ($c' = 0$) for triaxial compression and extension were surprisingly low at approximately 30° and 26°, respectively.

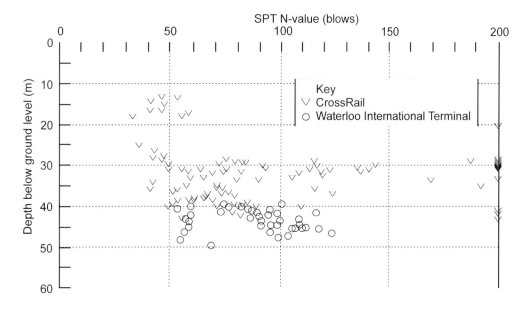

Figure 4.50 *Comparison of SPT data for Upper Mottled Clay at Waterloo International Terminal and Crossrail*

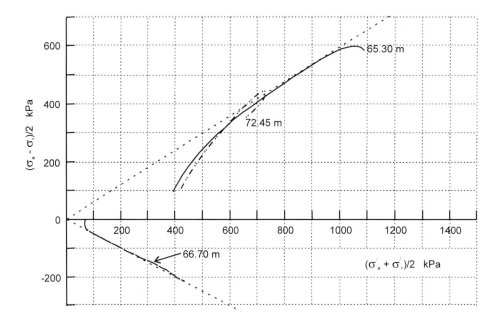

Figure 4.51 *Effective stress paths during undrained triaxial compression and extension of rotary cored samples of sand from the Lambeth Group at Sizewell*

4.13 EFFECTIVE STRESS STRENGTH PARAMETERS

The same difficulties apply to assessing the effective stress strength parameters of the different units of the Lambeth Group as apply to assessing undrained strength, namely:

● determining whether the data apply to material in its damaged or undamaged state

● the limited database, particularly for materials other than clays from the Upper and Lower Mottled Clays.

4.13.1 Upper and Lower Mottled Clays

A summary of the effective stress failure points in undrained triaxial compression tests with measurement of pore pressures, on samples from the Upper and Lower Mottled Clays, is presented in Figure 4.52.

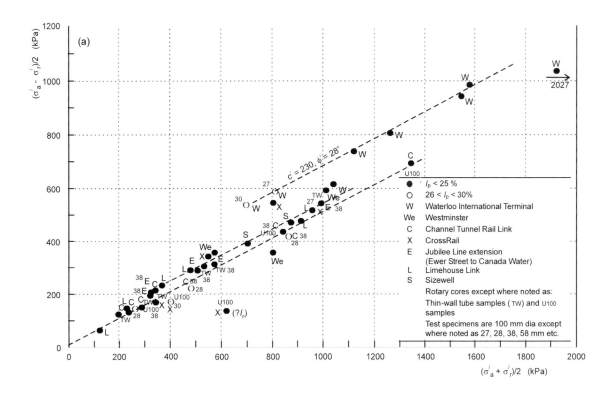

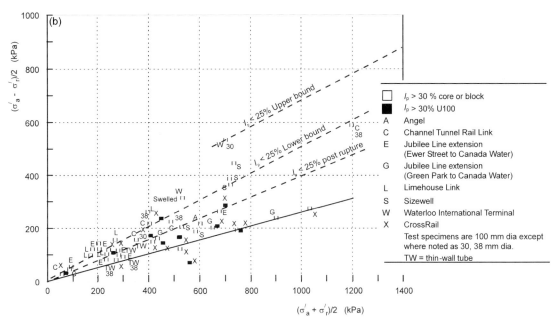

Figure 4.52 *Effective stress data at failure in undrained triaxial compression tests with pore pressure measurement. Upper and Lower Mottled Clays: (a) low-plasticity, (b) high-plasticity*

The data for low-plasticity clays (Figure 4.52(a)) and high-plasticity clays (Figure 4.52(b)) have been separated and a distinction made between rotary cored, thin-wall tube and U100 samples. Data from Westminster Station, CTRL, JLE, Angel Station and Sizewell has been added to those from Waterloo International Terminal and Crossrail, which were introduced in Section 4.12.

Comparison of the two figures confirms the important effect of soil plasticity. An upper bound to the data for the low-plasticity clays is provided by:

$$c' = 230 \text{ kPa} \qquad \varphi' = 28°$$

and an approximate lower bound by:

$$c' = 10 \text{ kPa} \qquad \varphi' = 28°$$

The spread of data between these two bounds reflects varying levels of cementing and of damage during sampling. Data for lower average effective stresses tend to cluster nearer to the lower bound, suggesting a reduction in cementing as a result of swelling, as discussed in Section 4.12.

Transferring these bounds to Figure 4.52(b) and adding the post-rupture failure line for the low-plasticity clays, it can be seen that, for the high-plasticity clays:

● only one data point lies on the peak envelope for the low-plasticity clays

● a better upper bound is provided by the lower bound to the low-plasticity clay data

● many of the data lie on or below the post-rupture failure line for low-plasticity clays

● a reasonable lower bound is given by:

$$c' = 0 \qquad \varphi' = 14.5°$$

As discussed above, the spread in data reflects natural variability in cementing, variability induced by sampling and the effects of polished fissures.

Data on effective stress strength parameters are also available for the Upper and Lower Mottled Clays from the following.

1 A series of isotropically consolidated drained triaxial compression tests on clay samples from Crossrail. The failure points are plotted in Figure 4.53 and can be seen to lie between the post-rupture failure line and the lower bound to the peak data for the low-plasticity clays.

2 Drained direct shear box (DSB) tests on 60 mm-square specimens, reported by Georgiannou *et al* (1993) and by Lehane *et al* (1995).

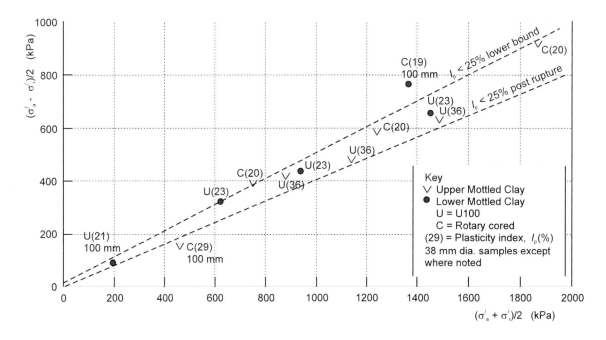

Figure 4.53 *Effective stress data at failure in isotropically consolidated drained triaxial compression tests. Upper and Lower Mottled Clays, Crossrail*

Georgiannou *et al* present the results of DSB tests on block clay samples of the Upper Mottled Clay, taken from below the axis level of the tunnel face, during reconstruction at Angel Station, Islington. The clay was of high plasticity (w_L = 73–75%, w_p = 31–32%, w_o = 18.0–18.3%) and was taken from just below the boundary with the overlying London Clay. (A profile of index properties at the site has been presented in Figure 4.23.) The results from the tests are shown in Figure 4.54 and illustrate the pronounced brittleness in the materials. The results define a peak failure envelope of c' = 110 kPa, φ' = 28° and a large strain or post-rupture failure envelope of c' = 22 kPa, φ' = 23.5° (Figure 4.55). The closely fissured plastic clay would appear to be cemented, although fissure orientation may have been such that they did not influence the results of the shear box test: failure was constrained to be on a horizontal plane, along which the material could have been intact. Triaxial tests on the same block samples from Angel gave results closer to the post-rupture envelope obtained from the DSB tests (Figure 4.55). In the triaxial test, the constraints imposed in the shear box test are lifted and the soil is able to fail in a variety of directions and would naturally fail on any unfavourably oriented weak surfaces. It is not clear if the weak surfaces on which failure took place in the triaxial tests were natural or were the result of yielding in the tunnel face (see Section 6.6). This comparison between DSB and triaxial test results on the Upper Mottled Clay from Angel illustrates the large anisotropy of strength that may be present as a result of weak surfaces.

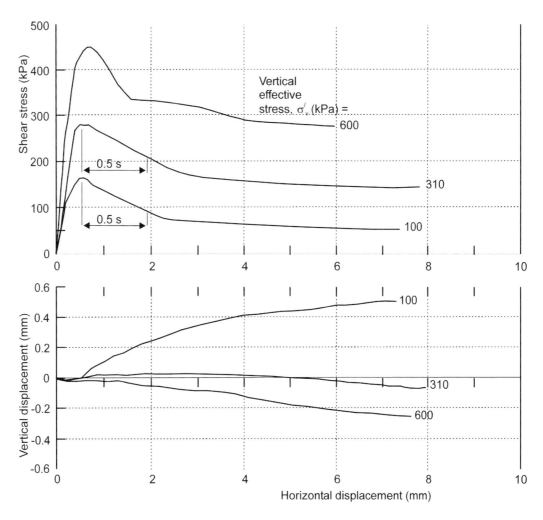

Figure 4.54 *Drained direct shear box test results on block sample of Upper Mottled Clay. Angel Station, Islington (after Georgiannou* et al, *1993)*

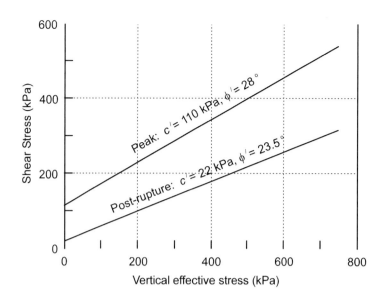

Figure 4.55 *Peak and post-rupture failure envelopes for direct shear box tests on Upper Mottled Clay. Angel Station, Islington (after Georgiannou et al, 1993)*

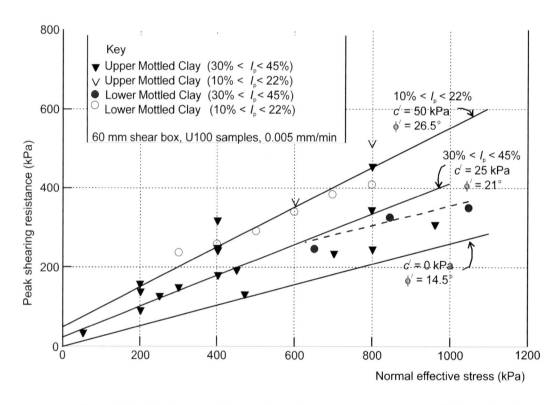

Figure 4.56 *Effective stress failure envelopes from direct shear box tests on U100 samples of Upper and Lower Mottled Clays, Crossrail (after Lehane et al, 1995)*

Lehane *et al* (1995) present the results of drained DSB tests on U100 clay samples of the Upper and Lower Mottled Clays from Crossrail. Their data and interpretation are shown in Figure 4.56. They suggest two failure envelopes, one of $c' = 50$ kPa, $\varphi' = 26.5°$, corresponding to clays of low plasticity ($10\% < I_p < 22\%$) and one of $c' = 25$ kPa, $\varphi' = 21°$, corresponding to clay of high plasticity ($30\% < I_p < 45\%$). It is probable that the U100 samples have suffered some damage, different to that suffered by block samples taken from a tunnel face. This could explain why the Crossrail data for the low-plasticity clays fall well below the upper bound peak failure envelope determined for low-plasticity clays in triaxial compression ($c' = 230$ kPa, $\varphi' = 28°$) and why data from the high-plasticity clays generally fall well below the peak failure envelope determined from shear box tests on block samples of the high-plasticity clay at Angel ($c' = 110$ kPa, $\varphi' = 28°$). It may be significant in Figure 4.55 that:

- several samples from the high-plasticity clay give strengths similar to those of the low-plasticity clay

- many of the data for the high-plasticity clay fall close to the post-rupture failure line obtained for both the low-plasticity clays in triaxial compression ($c' = 0$, $\varphi' = 23°$) and high-plasticity (Angel) clays in DSB tests ($c' = 22$ kPa, $\varphi' = 23.5°$)

- only one test result corresponds to the fissure strength failure envelope, thought to apply to the high-plasticity clays after swelling; the existence of a persistent horizontal polished fissure aligned with the mid-height of the shear box is presumed unlikely.

In summary, the data available on effective stress strength parameters for clays from the Upper and Lower Mottled Clays are as follows:

| | | Plasticity | | | |
| | | Low | | High | |
		c' (kPa)	φ' (°)	c' (kPa)	φ' (°)
Triaxial compression	Peak – upper bound	230	28	–	–
	Peak – lower bound	10	28	0	14.5
	Post-rupture	0	23	–	–
Direct shear box	Peak	50	26.5 [1]	110	28 [2]
				25	21
	Post-rupture			22	23

[1] U100   [2] Block

4.13.2 Laminated beds, Lower Shelly Clay, Upnor Formation

Data on peak effective stress strength parameters are available from drained and undrained triaxial compression tests run on samples from the Laminated beds, Lower Shelly Clay and Upnor Formation as part of the CTRL ground investigation. The data are summarised in Figures 4.57 to 4.59 and lead to the following parameters:

	c' (kPa)	φ' (°)
Laminated beds	0	21.5
Lower Shelly Clay	0	24 (reducing to $\varphi' = 16°$)
Upnor Formation	0	33 (reducing with increasing clay content)

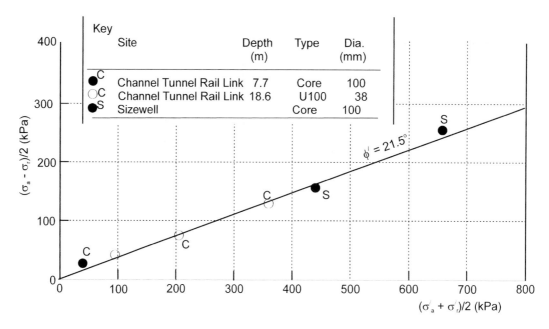

Figure 4.57 *Effective stress data at failure in triaxial compression tests. Laminated beds, CTRL and Sizewell*

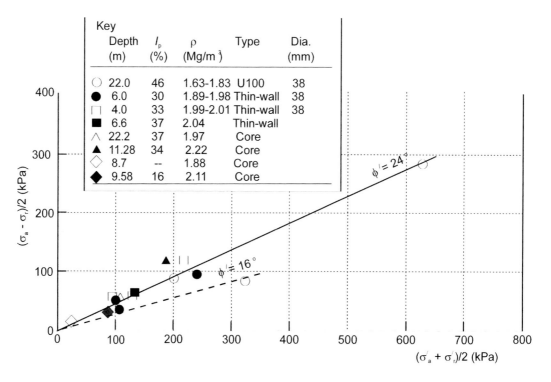

Figure 4.58 *Effective stress data at failure in triaxial compression tests. Lower Shelly Clay, CTRL*

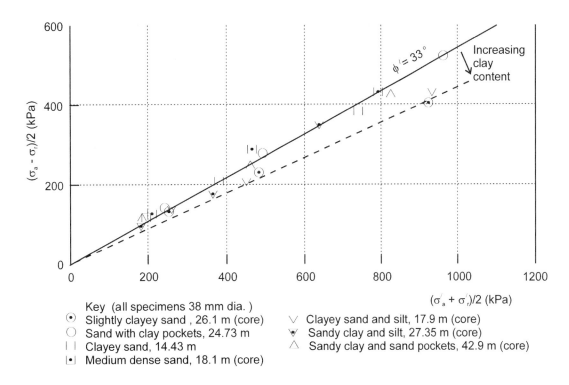

Key (all specimens 38 mm dia.)

⊙ Slightly clayey sand , 26.1 m (core)   ∨ Clayey sand and silt, 17.9 m (core)
○ Sand with clay pockets, 24.73 m   ⩔ Sandy clay and silt, 27.35 m (core)
⌇ Clayey sand, 14.43 m   △ Sandy clay and sand pockets, 42.9 m (core)
⌊•⌋ Medium dense sand, 18.1 m (core)

Figure 4.59 *Effective stress data at failure in triaxial compression tests. Upnor Formation, CTRL*

4.13.3   Residual strength

The shear box tests described by Lehane *et al* (1995) on samples from Crossrail were
continued, with reversals, to define the residual angle of shearing resistance, φ'_r. This
normally required a displacement of up to 20 mm. The measured values of φ'_r varied
with plasticity index as shown in Figure 4.60; this follows the normal pattern described
in Section 4.12 (see Figure 4.40). For high-plasticity samples ($I_p > 30\%$), Lehane *et al*
suggest $\varphi'_r \approx 11 \pm 3°$.

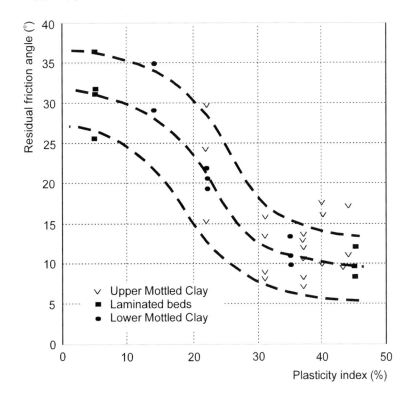

Figure 4.60 *Variation in residual angle of shearing resistance, φ'_r, with plasticity index, I_p,
Crossrail (after Lehane et al, 1995)*

4.14 **STIFFNESS**

4.14.1 **WIT and Angel Station: Upper Mottled Clay**

Small-strain stiffness data for both the low- and high-plasticity clays of the Upper Mottled Clay are available from undrained triaxial compression and extension tests, run with local instrumentation at Imperial College on rotary cored samples from WIT and block samples from Angel Station. The normalised stiffness characteristics are shown in Figures 4.61 and 4.62. The tests were run on samples that had been reconsolidated to estimated *in-situ* stresses, following the soil's recent stress history. Undrained shear, at a rate of 4.5 per cent/day was carried out after the drained creep rate in the samples had reduced to less than 0.045 per cent/day. For comparison, a band showing typical normalised shear stiffness data for London Clay has been added to Figure 4.61.

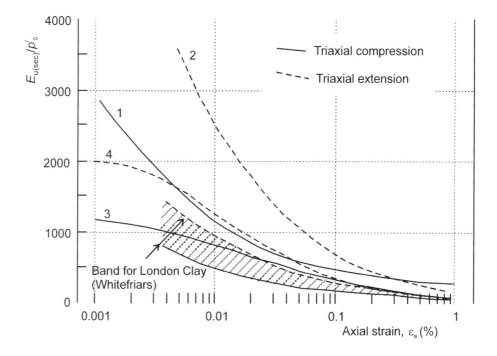

Test Depth from ground level	(m)	1 41-95–42.30	2 41.42–41.77	3 ~ 34.0	4 ~34.0
Site		Waterloo International Terminal		Angel Station	
Type of test		Triaxial compression	Triaxial extension	Triaxial compression	Triaxial extension
p'_i	(kPa)	65.5	144.7	>740	>800
w_L	(%)	32.5	34.5	72.6	74.7
w_P	(%)	13.5	13.6	30.6	31.5
I_P	(%)	19.0	20.9	42.0	43.0
w_0	(%)	11.5	10.2	26.1	23.5
I_L	(%)	-0.11	-0.16	-0.11	-0.19
ρ	(Mg/m^3)	2.28	2.29	2.01	2.06
σ'_{ac}	(kPa)	640	640	525	518
σ'_{rc}	(kPa)	557	557	524	517

Figure 4.61 *Non-linear shear stiffness characteristics for Upper Mottled Clay. Waterloo International Terminal and Angel Station*

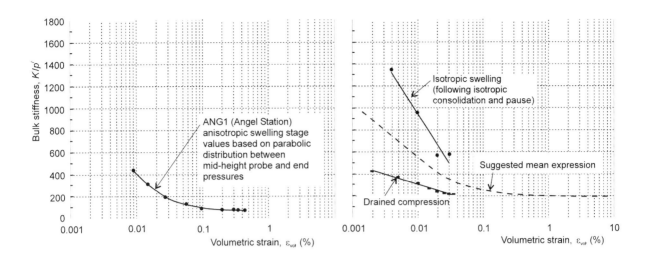

Figure 4.62 *Non-linear bulk stiffness characteristics for Upper Mottled Clay. Waterloo International Terminal and Angel Station*

The key stiffness characteristics are as follows:

		$E_{u\,0.1\%}/p'$	$L = E_{u\,0.1}/E_{u\,0.01}$	$E_{u\,0.01\,c}/E_{u\,0.01\,e}$
WIT	TC			
WIT	TE			
Angel	TC	820	0.415	0.648
Angel	TC	1265	0.20	
Typical London Clay values				

In comparing the results, it must be borne in mind that the block samples taken from the tunnel face at Angel may have been damaged by yielding in the face, see Section 6.6. It is clear that the normalised stiffness of the Upper Mottled Clay is considerably higher than that of London Clay. (The Upper Mottled Clay from Angel are of similar plasticity and liquidity index to the overlying London Clay, see Figure 4.19.) On the basis of these results, it would appear that the low-plasticity clays of the Upper Mottled Clay are stiffer than the high-plasticity clays, which is in line with normal findings.

4.14.2 Crossrail: Upper and Lower Mottled Clays

Stiffness data is also available from the Crossrail investigation, from triaxial compression tests on specimens with local instrumentation, reconsolidated to *in-situ* stresses (CAU) and from self-boring pressuremeter tests, interpreted following Jardine (1992). Envelopes to the data are presented in Figure 4.63.

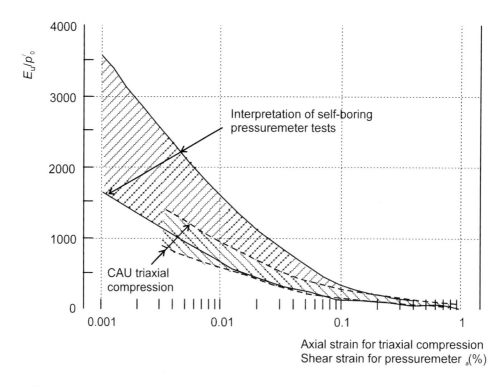

Figure 4.63 *Non-linear shear stiffness characteristics for Upper and Lower Mottled Clays, Crossrail*

4.14.3   JLE. Upper and Lower Mottled Clays, Laminated beds, Lower Shelly Clay, glauconitic sands

Stiffness data presented by Linney and Page (1996) from CAU triaxial compression and extension tests on thin-wall tube samples with local instrumentation are summarised in Figure 4.64.

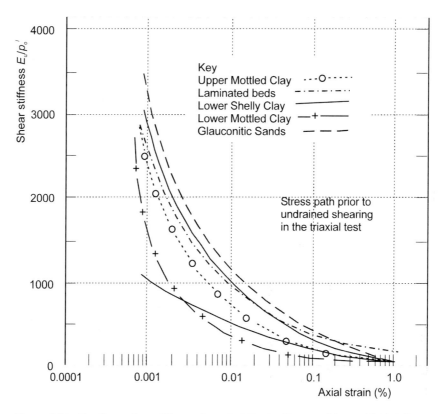

Figure 4.64 *Non-linear shear stiffness characteristics for Upper and Lower Mottled Clays, Laminated beds, Lower Shelly Clay and glauconitic sands, JLE*

4.14.4   Limehouse Link

Elastic shear moduli inferred from self-boring pressuremeter tests carried out at Limehouse Link are plotted in Figure 4.65. Shear modulus appears to increase with depth, the upper bound being approximately 60 MPa at the top of the unit and 200 MPa towards the base.

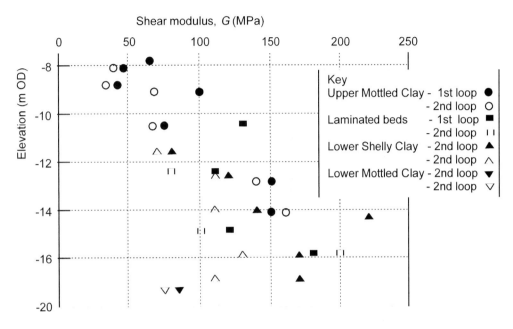

Figure 4.65 *Inferred elastic shear modulus values from self-boring pressuremeter tests, Limehouse Link*

In their back-analyses of the observed diaphragm wall movements during excavation for the Limehouse Link road tunnel, De Moor and Stevenson (1996) adopted drained Young's moduli for the Upper Mottled Clay (unit A), which were up to four times larger than for the overlying London Clay (360 MPa *cf* 90 MPa). The ratios were even larger for the Lower Shelly Clay (unit C) (400 MPa *cf* 90 MPa) and the Lower Mottled Clay (unit D) (600 MPa *cf* 90 MPa). (Equivalent values suggested for G/p' are 280 for London Clay and 600 for the clay units of the Lambeth Group.)

These back-analysed values are consistent with the upper bound for shear moduli from the pressuremeter tests, suggesting that the lower values from the pressuremeter may have been affected by disturbance.

4.14.5   Sizewell: body wave velocities and small strain shear moduli

At the site formerly considered for the Sizewell C Nuclear Power Station, an investigation was carried out into the body wave velocity and stiffness characteristics of the foundation soils, which included the Lambeth Group. *In-situ* measurements comprised shear and compression wave velocities using cross-hole and down-hole techniques, including the velocity of horizontally propagating, horizontally polarised shear waves. The methods of testing and the detailed results are presented by Hight *et al* (1997).

The general pattern of cross-hole velocities for the complete sequence is shown in Figure 4.66. At the location of the investigation, the Lambeth Group essentially comprised sand units. Shear and compression wave velocities in the Lambeth Group were higher than in the London Clay; V_{vh} ranged between 410 m/s and 500 m/s at the top of the formation and between 470 m/s and 540 m/s at the base. Taking the best estimate for V_{vh} as 480 m/s leads to G_{vh} of 472 MPa. In a previous investigation, where the Lambeth Group comprised clays, silts and sand, V_{vh} ranged between approximately 300 m/s and 450 m/s, giving a corresponding range in G_{vh} of 167–425 MPa.

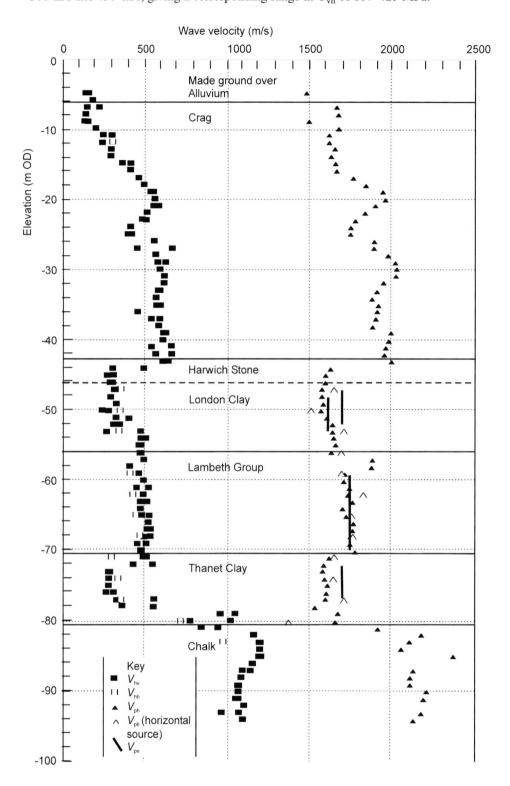

Figure 4.66 *Profiles of shear and compression wave velocities at Sizewell C (from Hight* et al, *1997)*

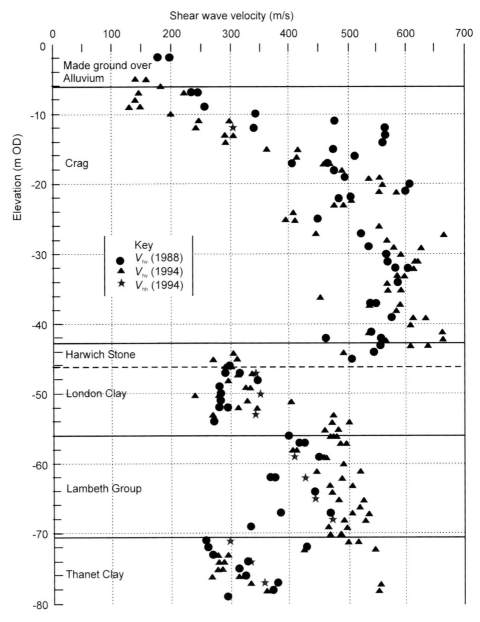

Figure 4.67 *Comparison of different shear wave velocities at Sizewell C (from Hight et al, 1997)*

Detailed comparisons of the different shear wave velocities are presented in Figure 4.67. At the centre of the Lambeth Group formation, the hierarchy of shear wave velocities was $V_{hh} < V_{vh} < V_{hv}$. The anisotropy of shear wave velocities and shear moduli was as follows:

	V_{vh}/V_{hv}	G_{vh}/G_{hv}	V_{hh}/V_{hv}	G_{hh}/G_{hv}
In-situ – sand	0.95	0.9	0.9	0.8
Lab – clay	0.9	0.8	0.9–1.0	0.8–1.0

4.15 PENETRATION RESISTANCE

4.15.1 SPT *N* values

The variations in SPT *N* value with depth for the different projects in the London Basin are shown in Figures 4.68 to 4.70. The cut-off value for *N* was 140 for Farringdon Station, 150 for JLE and 200 for Crossrail, CTRL and Newbury Bypass. The range of values for each project, and for each unit, is extremely large.

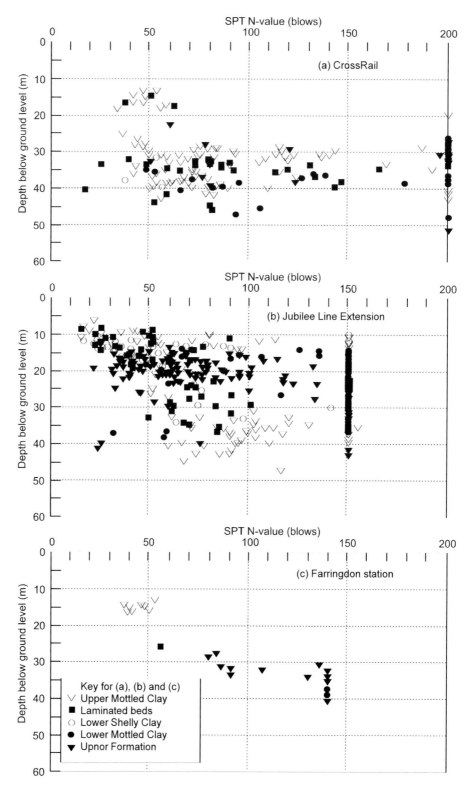

Figure 4.68 *Variation in SPT* N *value with depth. Crossrail, JLE and Farringdon Station*

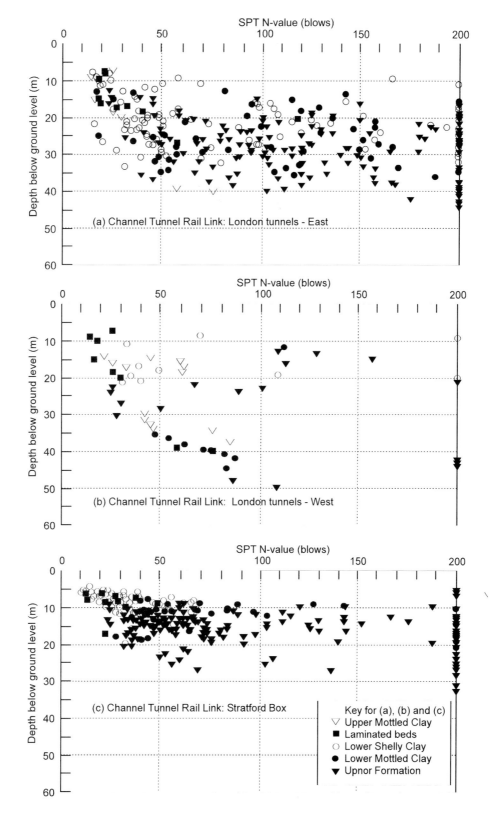

Figure 4.69 *Variation in SPT N value with depth, CTRL*

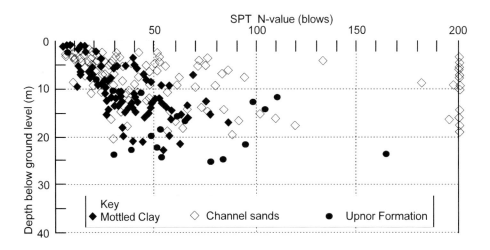

Figure 4.70 *Variation in SPT N value with depth, Newbury Bypass*

While the reproducibility of the test may be questioned, much of the variation must be real and reflects variations in:

- cementing, including the presence of limestone beds, duricrusts etc
- desiccation
- plasticity and fissure texture.

There is a tendency for lower values to be measured towards the top of the formation, which, at CTRL, where the upper units come close to the surface, is related to the effects of swelling to relatively low effective stresses. A reasonable lower bound can be identified, which approximately fits the data for each site and is given by:

$$N = 1.66\,D$$

where N = SPT value

D = depth below ground level (m)

Figures 4.71 and 4.72 show SPT data from two sites in central London, Waterloo International Terminal and Crossrail, where large thicknesses of London Clay overlie the Lambeth Group and for which SPT data are available for both formations. These illustrate graphically the differences between the formations, in particular the effect of the immediate post-depositional processes that took place in the Lambeth Group and not in the London Clay, namely desiccation and pedogenesis. These have given rise to much higher and much more variable SPT N values in the Lambeth Group. It is worth noting, however, that the lower bound to the London Clay data provides a continuation to the lower bound in the Lambeth Group. It is worth reflecting, also, on the complaints usually aimed at the variability in the London Clay.

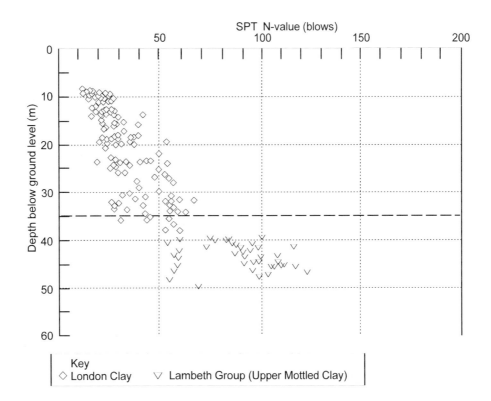

Figure 4.71 *Contrast between SPT* N *value in London Clay and Upper Mottled Clay, Waterloo International Terminal*

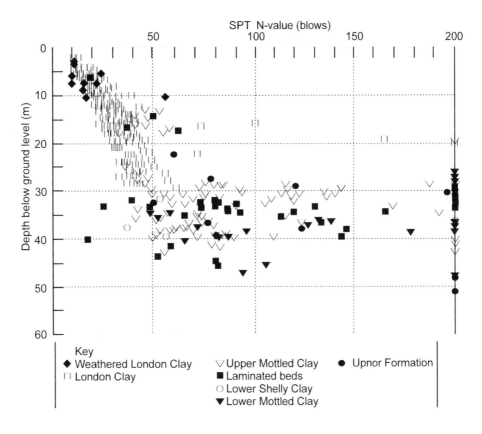

Figure 4.72 *Contrast between SPT* N *value in London Clay and Lambeth Group, Crossrail*

4.15.2   CPT

Examples of profiles of cone penetration resistance, q_c, sleeve friction, f_s, and friction ratio from measurements made at Stratford on the JLE are presented in Figure 4.73. Figure 4.73(a) shows the penetration record at a location where approximately 4 m of made ground and 12 m of London Clay overlie the Lambeth Group. Note how the penetration resistance q_c increases rapidly towards the base of the London Clay and on entering the Upper Mottled Clay of the Lambeth Group. This increase in resistance is consistent with the step in SPT values found on entering the Lambeth Group (see Figures 4.71 and 4.72).

Figure 4.73(b) presents the penetration record obtained when pushing through several units of the Lambeth Group, at a location where the top of the group is only 9 m below ground level. As would be expected, very distinct q_c and f_s signatures are associated with the different units. Note how the lower bound to q_c in the Lower Shelly and Mottled Beds forms a continuation of the q_c profile in the London Clay.

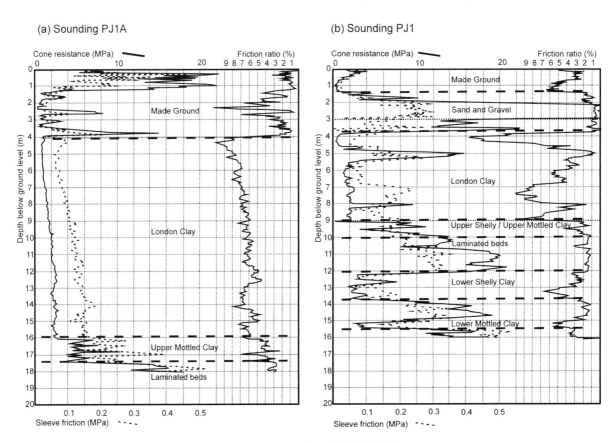

Figure 4.73 *CPT data, Stratford, JLE: (a) PJ1A, (b) PJ1*

4.15.3   SPT-CPT comparisons

The SPT N values measured in the ground investigations at Sizewell are plotted versus depth below top of stratum in Figure 4.74 (the top of the stratum is approximately 67 m below ground level. The usual variability is apparent, with higher values being recorded between 4 m and 7.5 m below top of stratum. At the site, a continuous cone penetration record was obtained into the Chalk. The section of the record through the Lambeth Group, and the London and Ormesby Clays immediately above and below the formation, is shown alongside the SPT data in Figure 4.74.

A similar comparison between SPT and CPT data can be made on the basis of information presented by Simpson *et al* (1979) for a site in central London, see Figure 4.75. Although the increase in SPT resistance is apparent on entering the Lambeth Group, the increase in q_c is less obvious.

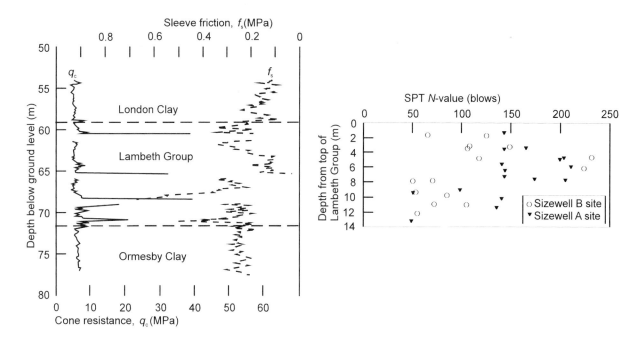

Figure 4.74 *SPT-CPT data comparison, Sizewell*

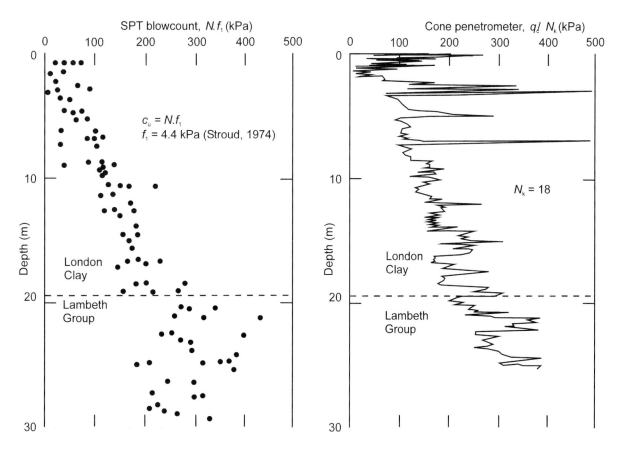

Figure 4.75 *SPT-CPT data comparison, central London (after Simpson* et al, *1979)*

4.16 CONSOLIDATION PARAMETERS

Conventional incremental load oedometer tests on samples from Crossrail and JLE give the following typical consolidation parameters.

	m_v [1] (m²/MN)	C_v (m²/year)
Upper Mottled Clay	0.02–0.08 [2]	0.06–2.0
Laminated beds	0.05–0.10	0.25
Lower Shelly Clay	0.015–0.05	0.6–0.7
Lower Mottled Clay	0.015–0.07	0.5–1.6

[1] $\sigma'v_o$ to $\sigma'v_o + 100\text{kPa}$ [2] reduces with depth

4.17 PERMEABILITY

A wide range in permeability can be expected for the units of the Lambeth Group, possibly between 3×10^{-4} m/s and 1×10^{-10} m/s.

The sand seams and fissures in the Upper and Lower Mottled Clays result in these beds having highly variable values of permeability, both spatially and with depth, and in the permeability being anisotropic.

Typical values of permeability measured in the Crossrail investigation were:

	k (m/s)
Upper Mottled Clay	$5 \times 10^{-7} - 5 \times 10^{-9}$
Laminated beds	$2 \times 10^{-7} - 3 \times 10^{-8}$
Lower Mottled Clay	1×10^{-8}
Glauconitic sand	$1 \times 10^{-8} - 4 \times 10^{-8}$

These may be compared with a range of permeabilities in the London Clay of 4.4×10^{-8} to 2.4×10^{-10} m/s.

Values measured in the Upnor Formation on CTRL were:

$k_h = 1 \times 10^{-4}$ to 1×10^{-5} m/s

$k_v = 1 \times 10^{-6}$ to 1×10^{-8} m/s.

5   Design, construction and performance

This section of the book presents information on the potential problems posed by the Lambeth Group and their treatment in various engineering scenarios. The factors controlling the behaviour of the Lambeth Group are identified where possible for each scenario in terms of design, construction and performance. Detailed case studies are presented to illustrate the direct influence the Lambeth Group has had on projects. The ground conditions described in the case studies have, where possible, been reinterpreted using the classification proposed in this book.

Information on the engineering performance of the Lambeth Group has been obtained from published literature, contributions made to the CIRIA study via a seminar held in October 1998, from personal discussions with the authors and from the author's experience.

5.1   BORED TUNNELS AND SHAFTS

5.1.1   History of construction

Tunnel construction within the Lambeth Group has a long and illustrious history, which began with early attempts to form tunnels beneath the River Thames in London in the early 19th century. Tunnels have been constructed within the Group for a variety of purposes including pedestrian access, highway and railway infrastructure, electrical and telecommunication (cable tunnels), mail handling, waste water, sewerage and water supply. The road tunnel at Limehouse Link, east London, is a cut-and-cover structure, which is dealt with in Section 5.2. Most tunnel construction has been in London, although the Lambeth Group has been encountered in recent waste water schemes on the south coast and in a flood alleviation scheme in Ipswich.

The earliest recorded tunnel driven through the Lambeth Group was the Thames Driftway (1805), which was constructed by hand from Rotherhithe, within the Upnor Formation. The tunnel was not completed as a result of serious runs of sand from the Laminated beds above the Lower Shelly Clay, as the cover of clay diminished (Skempton and Chrimes, 1994). The most famous tunnel within the Lambeth Group is Marc Isambard Brunel's Thames Tunnel from Rotherhithe to Wapping, built between 1825 and 1843. The tunnel was constructed using the first articulated tunnel shield (Mathewson and Laval, 1992; Skempton and Chrimes, 1994; Muir Wood, 1994) and was the world's first completed subaqueous tunnel. The tunnel is now occupied by London Underground's East London Line and has recently been refurbished. The meticulous records kept by Brunel and his engineers have recently been reinterpreted in an attempt to solve many of the questions regarding the actual geotechnical conditions encountered (Skempton and Chrimes, 1994). The ground investigation records and descriptions of the materials encountered in the tunnel face indicate that the tunnel was driven wholly within the Lambeth Group. The descriptions made have enabled the subdivisions of the group to be recognised. Borings undertaken from the ground investigation in 1824 indicated the geology of the chosen vertical alignment to comprise a good cover of tenacious clay above the tunnel crown and beneath the river bed, so much so that Brunel felt "satisfied that the ground is everywhere perfectly safe for the operation". During tunnelling, borings ahead of the tunnel were made. The borings revealed that the clay cover could not be relied on and additional borings were conducted over water. These borings revealed the full Lambeth Group sequence and the

Thanet Sand Formation "quicksand" beneath. There were five serious inundations of the tunnel, numerous falls of ground and large inflows of water. Runs of sand and silt (Laminated beds) were described from a horizon above the shelly clay (Lower Shelly Clay), which resulted in collapse of the overlying mottled beds (Upper Mottled Clay) and eventual flooding by the river. Falls also resulted from the overlying River Terrace Gravels impinging on the tunnel. One irruption caused the shield to be irrecoverably damaged, requiring replacement in 1835. Attempts were made to restrain the falls of ground and water inflows by placing bags filled with clay on the bed of the river; in addition, poling boards were placed ahead of the shield to support the face. Tunnelling conditions improved when the clay cover above the tunnel and the strength of the clay increased as the Wapping shore was approached.

The development of underground construction has gone very much hand in hand with the implementation of innovative tunnelling techniques and geotechnical processes. Appendix 3 presents a summary of the key bored tunnels constructed within the Lambeth Group. Bored tunnels have been constructed using a variety of methods: hand mining, with or without the protection of a shield; open-face tunnel boring machine; shield with roadheader or backhoe; slurry machine, earth pressure balance machine (EPBM) and microtunnelling. The shotcrete support method (sprayed concrete lining, SCL) or New Austrian Tunnelling Method (NATM) has only been applied in a tunnel partially within the Lambeth Group at London Bridge on the Jubilee Line Extension. The choice of the tunnelling method is varied and reflects the level of technology available, the required size, the lining type erected and the anticipated nature of the Lambeth Group, in particular its permeability. Pressurised closed forms of tunnelling, using either an EPBM or slurry machine, have only recently been used in the Group. Before the development of these forms of tunnelling machines, tunnels had been constructed using techniques where the ground was open and exposed at the face. This form of tunnelling is made difficult by the presence of water-bearing granular strata without recourse to geotechnical processes, such as grouting or compressed air. This fact restricted the development of London's underground railway system into south-east London and into the subcrop of the Lambeth Group.

5.1.2   Tunnel and shaft lining design

Bored tunnel lining design in the UK, which generally follows the design principles of Muir Wood (1975) and Curtis (1976), is governed by the relative magnitude of the *in-situ* stresses (σ_v and σ_h), and the elastic modulus of the ground (E). These determine the hoop load and maximum and minimum bending moments. Appropriate values of σ_v, σ_h and E are difficult to determine in tunnelling applications where the creation of a void alters both the *in-situ* stresses and the stiffness. Bored tunnels are now typically lined with pre-cast concrete segments or pipes jacked into place. Until the Second World War, tunnels and shafts were lined with cast iron.

Case history data indicate that the values of K_o adopted for design of tunnels in the Lambeth Group has varied from 0.75 to 2.0.

It is generally recognised that tunnelling in overconsolidated clays leads to an immediate reduction from K_o upon excavation to a value K_h, which upon completion of the lining then slowly increases in time. Measurements from instrumented linings in London Clay indicate that K_h has yet to reach unity. Values in uncemented clayey or silty sands are often lower than this, being based on the conservative assumption that these materials are normally consolidated since this yields a greater bending moment.

The design of the tunnel lining for the Thames Water Ring Main in the Lambeth Group (Farrow and Claye, 1994) considered that full K_o could develop and the linings were designed for a normal K_o of 1.75 and an extreme of 2.0. The linings were unreinforced and used high-strength concrete of 60 N/mm^2 and 85 N/mm^2 for the 150+ year design life at depths up to 75 m.

The 3.81 m-diameter 600 mm-long expanded concrete running tunnel linings for the Jubilee Line were designed for a K_o of 1.5 (Lyons, 1979). The Three Valleys Water tunnel (Baker and James, 1990) was designed with a K_o of 0.75.

Lining design is not so sensitive to stiffness as *in-situ* stresses. However, for design it is preferable to know the range of stiffness for the material so that this sensitivity can be assessed.

Tunnel linings have been designed to make the tunnel watertight through the variable and frequently water-bearing ground conditions, incorporating measures such as grommetted bolts, gaskets, hydrophilic seals, grout holes and caulking grooves. Packing between the vertical joints (often used to correct for misalignment) is avoided because it provides a potential point of water ingress and butted or bolted joints are preferred. Misalignment can be removed by the use of tapered segments.

As the Lambeth Group is frequently water-bearing, the lining often has to be built within a tailskin necessitating bolted segments. Expanded linings have been built, but their use is restricted to open tunnelling techniques where the integrity of the cut surface can be guaranteed.

Provided that normal assessments are made for the correct selection of construction materials, tunnel and shaft linings erected within the Lambeth Group have generally not shown signs of corrosion. There is one notable exception, however: the grey cast iron linings erected for the Northern Line in 1901 (and later rebuilt in 1922–1924) between Old Street and Moorgate (Case Study 5.1).

Following an assessment of the risk of potential groundwater rise within London, tunnel linings within the relatively high-permeability granular strata, were considered at greater risk of damage, due to larger and more rapid pore pressure changes within them (Simpson *et al*, 1989). Tunnels previously constructed in granular strata that have subsequently dried out and become oxidised (due to groundwater lowering) are at risk from the form of chemical attack described in Case Study 5.1. New tunnels that are to be constructed within these materials should be designed to take into account such effects of long-term changes in the groundwater regime.

A condition of the tunnel linings selected for the Jubilee Line Extension through the Lambeth Group was the requirement for low-permeability concrete with low diffusivity to chloride and oxygen ions (Davies and Coutts, 1994). To avoid the type of problems experienced at Old Street, further durability was achieved by increasing concrete cover to a minimum of 40 mm, avoiding cast-in ferrous items and using a high-grade concrete.

The London Underground tunnels were constructed in the late 19th century some 25 m beneath City Road, originally as the City and South London Railway. Between 1922 and 1924 these tunnels were widened to take the larger rolling stock of the London Electric Railway. Cracking of the cast iron lining was first noted in 1962 and has necessitated several phases of investigation and remedial work, the results from which have been well documented and reviewed by Mather (1986), Rainey and Rosenbaum (1989) and Bracegirdle *et al* (1996b).

The cracking has been associated with leakages of strongly acidic water (which also contains a high proportion of sulphate) and the development of yellow encrustations on the lining surface. The cause has been attributed to the unusual geology since the tunnels lie within a sand channel feature within the Upper Mottled Clay of the Lambeth Group, immediately below the London Clay. The reason for the corrosion and cracking of the lining has been subject to some debate, but is thought to be due to chemical reactions between iron pyrites (naturally occurring within the sand channel) and the grout behind the tunnel linings within the presence of oxidising bacteria (Bracegirdle *et al*, 1996a). The reactions generate sulphuric acid, which corrodes the tunnel lining and further promotes the reaction with the lime grout. Precipitates of thaumasite and ettringite caused volumetric changes, which cracked the iron lining. The lowering of groundwater in the past, due to industrial abstraction, is considered to have promoted oxidation.

The engineering solutions to this problem have included steel straps, which were later replaced by steel beams as the deterioration continued, injection of alkaline solutions to neutralise the acid groundwater and the injection of pulverised fuel ash into cavities generated behind the lining (Bracegirdle *et al*, 1996). In 1994, London Underground instigated a programme to replace the damaged tunnel linings over a section of 160 m, coincident with the excavation of the tunnel in the sand lens. Detailed mineralogical analyses were undertaken to choose new construction materials inert to corrosion by the acid. The lining was eventually replaced with a stainless steel lining, which, at a cost of £12 million, is the most expensive tunnel lining ever constructed.

5.1.3 Tunnel construction

Successful tunnel construction depends on correct selection of the tunnelling method (excavation and lining), which in turn requires knowledge of the ground conditions and how the ground will behave. Problems frequently occur where the behaviour was not anticipated.

Hard ground

Hard ground has been encountered on numerous tunnels constructed within the Lambeth Group. Known hard bands have now been identified and are associated with particular stratigraphical horizons and subunits. The duricrust that occurs at the mid-Lambeth Group hiatus has been a significant problem. In the Thames Tunnel the duricrust (chalk) required chisels to break it up into lumps. In the first Blackwall Tunnel crossing pieces of large rock embedded in the sands beneath the London Clay caused damage to the cutting edge, requiring its replacement, and, at the centre of the river, excavation of the chalk (ie duricrust) required more time to excavate. Harding (1981) describes the Upper Mottled Clay as being very hard, causing the fracture of the cutting edges on the shields used to construct the Northern Line extension from Euston to Camden Town in 1923, leaving the miners to complete the tunnel by hand. Flint, which is present in high concentrations at a number of stratigraphical horizons within the Lambeth Group, can be a hazard because of its high abrasivity. The most notable occurrence of flint gravel is in the pebble bed, which lies immediately below the Lower Mottled Clays in east London and is known to be cemented.

Groundwater control

Granular water-bearing horizons are a common feature of tunnelling in the Lambeth Group. In London, such horizons are often associated with channel sand bodies located at the interface of the London Clay and Lambeth Group (the precise stratigraphical position is not known but could possibly be the Harwich Formation or Upper Shelly Clay), within the Upper Mottled Clay, the Laminated beds, sandy laminae within the Lower Shelly Clay and the Upnor Formation. Granular and potentially water-bearing ground creates problems such as face instability, which may:

- preclude safe excavation and erection of lining

- increase the risk of collapse and/or increased surface settlement

- promote tailskin instability, which may prevent erection of a particular lining type

- increase the risk of flooding and inundation

- make for poorer working conditions and create unacceptable risks to construction on health and safety grounds.

The greatest risk occurs when these conditions are encountered having not been anticipated prior to construction. Where anticipated, water-bearing ground conditions will influence the choice of the tunnelling method. Various geotechnical processes have been adopted to progress tunnel construction through these conditions. Many of the techniques are not new but have continued to be used to the present day. Table 5.1 lists the various tunnelling methods and supporting geotechnical processes that have been used in the Lambeth Group, either singly or in combination.

Table 5.1   *Tunnelling methods adopted in the Lambeth Group and supporting geotechnical processes*

Tunnelling method	**Geotechnical processes**
Shield with hand mining, backhoe or roadheader (typically used on long drives)	Compressed air Dewatering Permeation grouting.
Hand mining (typically used for complex geometries and openings)	Compressed air Dewatering Permeation grouting.
Earth pressure balance machine	Not required
Slurry machine	Not required

Where granular and water-bearing ground was encountered within the Thames Tunnel, Brunel adopted the use of forepoling and close timbering, but conditions must have remained extremely difficult since he could not control the groundwater. Compressed air was first used in a tunnel within the Lambeth Group beneath the Thames at Greenwich in 1899, having first been used in 1879 in Belgium (West, 1988). (A second tunnel was driven recently for the Docklands Light Railway using a 5.6 m-diameter slurry machine.) Compressed air is used to balance the hydrostatic pressure of groundwater within granular or water-bearing strata, thus providing face stability to enable the safe excavation and the erection of tunnel lining, or to carry out other operations such as gaining safe access to the face. Details of the ground conditions through which compressed air was successfully applied on the Central Line extension to Ilford, west of Stratford, are presented in Figure 5.1. Some 10 000 rings were erected between Bow and Leyton within the Lambeth Group using compressed air and 12 ft-diameter hooded shields (Harding, 1981).

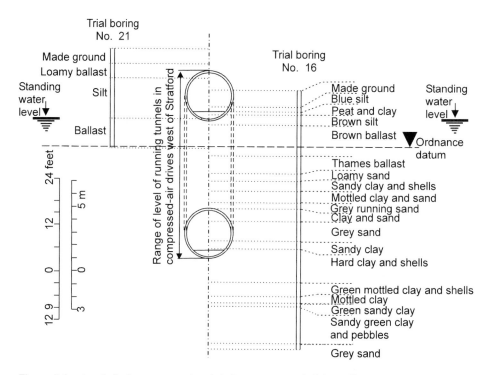

Figure 5.1 *Lambeth Group encountered during compressed air tunnelling west of Stratford Station on the Central Line*

Compressed air is still considered to be a reliable means to control groundwater in granular strata and was adopted as the preferred method of construction on the Jubilee Line Extension for the enlargement of 4.45 m internal diameter running tunnels to 8.0 m internal diameter station tunnels at Bermondsey, and for the construction of cross-passages beneath the River Thames for the Docklands Light Railway extension to Greenwich.

The use of compressed air is governed by The Work in Compressed Air Regulations 1996 and BS 6164. Its application in tunnelling is also influenced by the following factors:

● where it is not possible to adopt pressurised closed forms of mechanical tunnelling, perhaps due to an unanticipated change in ground conditions

● where other geotechnical processes are not appropriate or cannot be used, either because of the relative size of the area of the works, or because, for example, access cannot be obtained for permeation grouting.

The pressure of compressed air applied is usually based on the reliable measurement of pore water pressure in adjacent boreholes, to determine the hydrostatic pressure at the tunnel face. Difficulties have been experienced in the correct interpretation of these pressures, as a result of poor selection and maintenance of instrumentation.

Compressed air has been used in combination with other forms of treatment such as grouting (see Case study 5.2 and Case study 5.3) and dewatering (see Case study 5.3). The variable success of compressed air is described in Case study 5.3. The failure of grouting and the measures undertaken to construct a tunnel in the upper part of the Lambeth Group and a pingo remnant are described in Case study 5.4.

Construction of the Second Blackwall Crossing using permeation grouting and compressed air (Caron *et al*, 1963)

The alignment of the second Blackwall Tunnel (Kell and Ridley, 1966) took it through the Laminated beds, London Clay and a large gravel-filled scour structure, which penetrates through to the Lambeth Group, situated close to the confluence of the River Lea with the Thames. The invert of the tunnel would pass through or very close to the top of the Laminated beds, which comprise silty fine sand over the northern part of the tunnel (Figure 5.2a).

A 7 ft (2.13 m)-diameter pilot tunnel was driven within the overlying London Clay from which grouting operations were carried out in the Laminated beds and also the overlying River Terrace Gravel. Ten *in-situ* permeability tests gave values of k between 1 to 7×10^{-6} m/s for the Laminated beds. The range of particle size distribution of the silty sand is shown in Figure 5.2b with samples of sand that had been successfully treated. The investigations revealed that the sand was too fine to be treated with sodium silicate grout and so a resin treatment was employed. Injections were carried out radially from the tunnel through specially designed cast iron rings incorporating grout ports.

Following a trial, a *tube-à-manchette* system was used to deliver the grout. Grout lances failed because of the presence of the Blackheath Beds, which damaged the pipes. Also, the low permeability of the material being treated meant there was a tendency for the grout to travel back up the lance. The procedures employed to treat the ground systematically are described in the paper. This treatment, which was the first application of resin grouting in the UK, enabled the tunnel to be constructed essentially in the dry. Compressed air was used where there was some seepage, as a precaution. However, at Poplar the cover was too shallow to balance the water pressures in the Laminated beds and the ground treatment enabled the tunnel to be completed in free air.

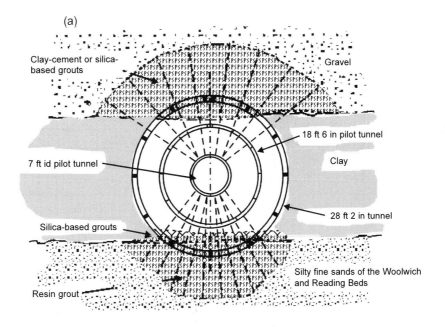

(a)

Figure 5.2a *Ground treatment carried out on the Second Blackwall Tunnel: pattern of ground treatment adopted at the northern end of the tunnel (Poplar)*

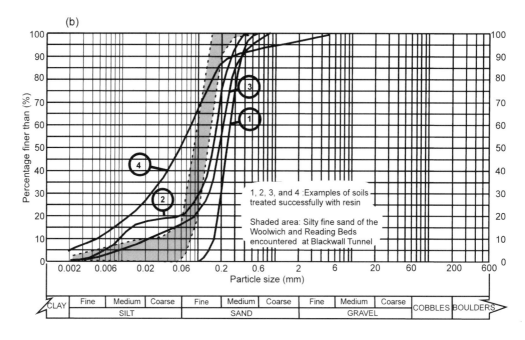

Figure 5.2b   *Ground treatment carried out on the Second Blackwall Tunnel: particle size distribution curves of treated Laminated beds*

Construction of the Northern Line tunnels in 1905, their subsequent modification in 1923 (Harding, 1981) and the construction of the Victoria Line 40 years later (Follenfant *et al*, 1969), near Euston

Case study 5.3

Near Euston, the thickness of the London Clay is reduced to 9 m or less and the alignments of both the Northern and Victoria Lines lie within or close to the Lambeth Group. The presence of channel sand bodies within the Upper Mottled Clay has strongly influenced the construction of these tunnels. Furthermore, the various tunnels and investigations have allowed the extent and shape of these sand bodies to be conjectured. Compressed air, dewatering and grouting were all used to control groundwater, although compressed air had but limited success.

Barrow (1905) described the ground conditions experienced during the construction of the Northern Line tunnel as follows:

> *...between Euston and Hampstead a considerable amount of water was met within some sand beds in the middle of the Mottled Reading Clay (Reading Formation [Upper Mottled Clay]). To keep out the water the work was carried on under air pressure for a considerable time. The water bearing beds vary in thickness from as much as 15 ft to a foot or two, and apparently die away altogether at times. They have a constantly rising and falling surface...*

During the construction of the extension from Euston to Camden in 1923 the sands in the Upper Mottled Clay were met again. Although anticipated, their actual location was not known precisely and it was necessary, as a contingency, to have compressed air equipment available from the outset. Harding (1981) described slow tunnelling progress through the water-bearing sand and the miners remained extremely cautious of the stability of the sand in compressed air.

The sands were also encountered during the construction of the Victoria Line. Although anticipated, their location could not be determined precisely and probing ahead was undertaken. Compressed air was adopted during the construction of the new low-level tunnels when the sands were water-bearing. However, problems arose during the construction of the step plate junctions, which involved

CIRIA C583

encircling the existing Northern Line tunnels, when compressed air could not be used. Since the geometry of the sand body was not known, it was difficult to dewater the sand and water ingress persisted until the source of the water was eventually determined.

The 9.145 m-diameter step plate junction beneath Somers Town Goods Yard encountered sand channels within the Upper Mottled Clay when water and silty sand dramatically burst into the face (Figure 5.3). Compressed air could not provide sufficient control and a 2.13 m pilot tunnel was driven along the interface of the sand and the underlying clay. Perforated pipes were pushed through previously drilled boreholes into the sand. The pipes were connected to a manifold and vacuum pump and the sand dewatered. However, boreholes undertaken from the surface indicated that the sand lens extended beyond an old running tunnel, beyond the reach of the dewatering probes. Therefore, ground treatment was carried out from the surface using *tubes-à-manchettes* installed on a 1.5 m grid. Cement bentonite grouting was initially undertaken to prevent heave and this was followed by resin permeation grouting. Although uneven, the treatment was satisfactory, allowing poling and the chambers to be completed (Follenfant *et al*, 1969).

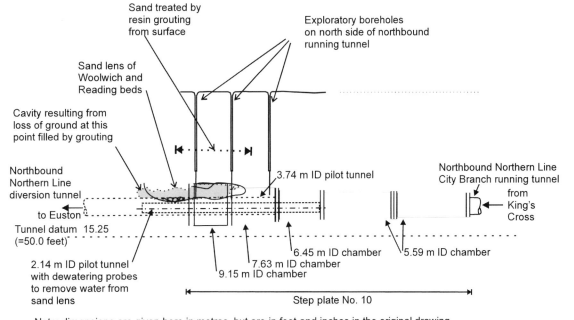

Note: dimensions are given here in metres, but are in feet and inches in the original drawing

Figure 5.3 *Step plate junction No 10 near Euston showing relative location of a sand lens encountered during tunnelling (Follenfant* et al, *1969)*

Three Valleys Water Tunnel, Wraysbury to Iver, West London (Baker and James, 1990)

To provide a supply of raw water to Thames Water's Iver treatment works, a 2.54 m internal diameter 6 km-long tunnel was driven to connect with outlets from Wraysbury and Datchet Reservoirs. The tunnel was for the most part within the London Clay, although a length of 600 m within the Lambeth Group was anticipated, but no higher than tunnel axis level.

The tunnel was constructed with an open face shield and a backhoe and lined with an expanded pre-cast concrete wedge-block lining. Difficulties were experienced with the excavation of a 600 mm-thick siltstone bed (possibly Harwich Formation or Upper Shelly Clay), which was only picked up in one of the cable percussion boreholes. The 150 mm-thick water-bearing pebble bed (Harwich Formation) caused the cut profile to slough, thus preventing the wedge-block lining system to be used efficiently. Consequently, the lining system changed to a bolted pre-cast concrete lining; compressed air was used to control groundwater.

Concern that the Lambeth Group would rise higher in the tunnel prompted additional ground investigation (cable percussion boreholes), which discovered the presence of a pingo remnant (Figure 5.4). The anomaly occupied a 55 m length of the tunnel alignment and was partly filled with highly variable downwashed river terrace gravels and upthrust Lambeth Group sands, silts and clays. Artesian groundwater pressures were measured within two of the sand layers. The pingo remnant presented a formidable obstacle to safe tunnelling and the decision was chosen to treat the feature using a combination of cement bentonite and silicate grouting.

Unfortunately, grouting of the low-permeability silty sands (generally $< 10^{-5}$ m/s) resulted in poor mixing of the silicate gel and the hardener and the ground failed to stabilise. A rolling pattern of ground freezing was implemented using liquid nitrogen. The tunnel was safely driven through the frozen ground.

The presence of the pingo remnant within 40 m of an existing borehole raised the question of whether a further anomaly could be encountered. Seismic reflection surveys were undertaken and these confirmed the continuity of strata along the alignment (Figure 5.5). The change in anticipated ground conditions resulted in an increase in expenditure during construction of 83 per cent.

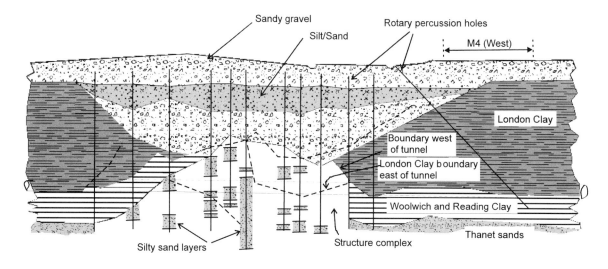

Figure 5.4 *Pingo remnant located on Three Valleys Tunnel, west London (Baker and James, 1990)*

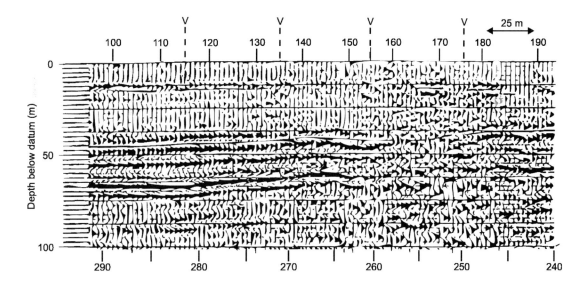

Figure 5.5 *Seismic reflection survey along section of the Three Valleys Tunnel. Note the prominent reflectors in the Lambeth Group (Baker and James, 1990)*

The decision to adopt compressed air within the Reading Formation for the treatment of water-bearing channel sand structures is a difficult one. Mair *et al* (1997) describe the deliberations made in assessing the potential water-bearing nature and face stability of these sand lenses for the Angel Station development. Reference was made to descriptions made during the tunnelling operations for both initial construction (1900–1907) and subsequent modification (1922–1924). On the basis of this desk study, it was decided to carry out the recent reconstruction in free cut, without recourse to any geotechnical process. No stability problems were reported.

Spoil behaviour and handling

The selection of the form of pressure balance tunnel machine is important through lithologically variable ground. For JLE Contract 105, from Bermondsey to Canada Water, the contractor chose to use an earth pressure balance machine though the upper strata of the Lambeth Group, which were predominantly clays. For the DLR Lewisham Extension the contractor chose to use a slurry machine through the Lambeth Group. The two projects were within 3.5 km of each other, but the slurry machine would encounter the less cohesive Upnor Formation, Thanet Sand Formation and the river terrace gravel and this influenced the selection of the machine. Ferguson *et al* (1991) describe two drives constructed with a slurry shield TBM and pipejacking for the Royal Docks Drainage Scheme. Where the machines were excavating within clay, tunnel production was reduced since the naturally occurring clay clogged the intake pipes.

For these types of tunnelling machine the behaviour of the spoil is important in terms of performance, since it forms an integral part of the success of the tunnelling method. Modern pressurised tunnelling machines often use conditioners or additives, such as deflocculants, to assist in spoil handling. The behaviour of the spoil together with any additives should be evaluated prior to their use. Slurry machines use separation equipment to recondition the slurry for reuse. Due consideration should be given to the selection of this machinery for the ground conditions anticipated.

Gases

Tunnelling in the sand within the Reading Formation for the Victoria Line frequently required the use of compressed air. On one occasion the compressed air displaced the atmosphere from the voids in the sand beds into a neighbouring tunnel being driven in free air, reducing the oxygen content and increasing the nitrogen content, to dangerously low levels. A similar occurrence within the silty sand within the Lambeth Group occurred during the construction of a cable tunnel beneath Tottenham Court Road in 1951, where the problem was exacerbated by low barometric pressure.

Glauconite rapidly oxidises on exposure to air and in a confined environment within a tunnel this may lead to the reduction of oxygen in the air. Two deaths were reported due to such an occurrence on the Thames Water Ring Main. The need to recognise such conditions is consequently emphasised in BS 6164. Lewis and Harris (in preparation) report on the identification of potentially deoxygenated gases during the investigation for the North London Flood Relief Sewer. Gas monitoring identified oxygen depletion within the Upnor Formation, where the piezometric elevation was below the top of the unit. The degree of depletion measured was dependent on the barometric pressure. A risk analysis was performed before construction to evaluate the effects of this condition during tunnel construction. Forced ventilation and continuous gas monitoring were subsequently provided during construction. Similar low oxygen contents have been encountered in the Upnor Formation where dewatered.

While there is a significant organic content within lignitic horizons in the Lambeth Group, it is not known whether such material could yield methane in sufficient concentrations to exceed the lower explosive limit.

Ground movements

The prediction of the effects of tunnel construction in an urban environment is an important aspect in the planning and control of the work. Tunnel construction in soft ground usually results in the development of a trough of settlement that, if of sufficient curvature, could potentially damage structures or services. Modern methods of prediction are used to determine the size and shape of the settlement trough. From this strains can be determined for assessing the potential damage to buildings (Mair *et al*, 1996; Potts and Addenbrooke, 1996) or services (Bracegirdle *et al*, 1996b).

There are very few published data on the performance of tunnelling wholly within the Lambeth Group. Measurements of the performance of a 5 m-diameter earth pressure balance machine through the Lambeth Group were made as part of the CIRIA-led LINK-CMR research project at Southwark Park on the Jubilee Line Extension (Burland *et al*, 1996). Figure 5.6 presents the results of immediate short-term vertical surface movement due to tunnel construction at a depth to axis of approximately 21 m.

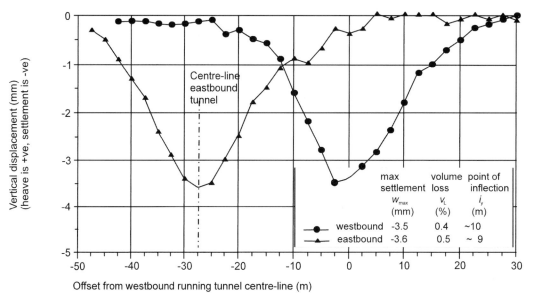

Figure 5.6 *Ground settlement profile measured at Southwark Park*

The measured ground movements were substantially less than those predicted based on the design volume loss of 2 per cent. A volume loss of between 0.4 and 0.5 per cent can be equated to these results. The results indicate either a stiffer response from the ground than predicted or good earth pressure control of the *in-situ* stresses and granular water bearing ground. The selection of values for volume loss and trough width appropriate for planning and design requires considerable judgement.

5.1.4   Shaft construction

Access to bored tunnels is normally given by shafts constructed from the surface. They have been constructed through the Lambeth Group in a variety of ways including: wet caissons, underpinning, jacking, diaphragm walls, sheet and bored pile walls. They have been lined with brick, cast iron segments, *in-situ* concrete, sheet piles and pre-cast concrete.

The design and construction of shafts is often the responsibility of the contractor as they usually form part of the temporary works, although they are often incorporated into the permanent works.

A number of problems have been encountered during the construction of shafts within the Lambeth Group. A summary of the major case study data for shaft construction through the Lambeth Group is given in Appendix 3. The Rotherhithe Shaft, built for the Thames Tunnel by Brunel, was constructed of brickwork and was sunk as a wet caisson through the overlying deposits into the Lambeth Group, where the shaft was completed by underlaying – excavating and then building successive courses of brickwork. Groundwater was a problem in the Upnor Formation and sheet piling had to be driven ahead of the lowest section. The Laminated beds, which were later to prove troublesome during tunnel excavation, were found to be dry (Skempton and Chrimes, 1994).

The 18 m × 12 m (60 ft × 40 ft) × 24 m (80 ft)-deep ventilation shaft at Poplar for the Second Blackwall Crossing was constructed as a concrete caisson with an outer skin of mild steel plate. It was sunk by blowing down under compressed air through the Lambeth Group. By contrast similar shafts in the London Clay were completed in free air.

Two shafts for the Victoria Line at Euston encountered a 2.4 m lens of silty sand within the Upper Mottled Clay, although the shaft for Euston Station encountered just clay. To avoid delay in installing vertical air locks the shafts were sunk in free air, with considerable difficulty, the first by normal mining methods and the second by jacking down rings of pre-cast concrete segments. Both shafts remained wet until caulked.

Construction of shafts for the Royal Docks Drainage Scheme were hindered by the presence of rock ledges, which required up to 300 tonnes of kentledge and heavy underwater chiselling to free the wet caissons (Ferguson *et al*, 1991). To avoid the potential problem of the 12 m × 22 m × 35 m-deep concrete caisson shaft at Durand's Wharf for the JLE hanging up on hard bands in the Lambeth Group, a slurry trench was pre-excavated using diaphragm wall equipment. Shafts sunk within the Lambeth Group outlier at Shoreham, West Sussex. Difficulties were experienced where lignite and fossilised trees were encountered in excavating through the Woolwich Formation.

5.1.5   Bored tunnels and shafts: key points

1   Because of the variable and often unpredictable nature of the Lambeth Group, tunnels have, where possible, been sited clear, for example by raising the alignment into the overlying London Clay or superficial deposits. This has the advantage that the tunnels are constructed within one tunnelling medium for which the tunnelling method (excavation and lining) is selected. Problems occur and costs increase when there is a change in conditions or mixed faces and the original method is no longer appropriate.

2   Where tunnels are to be constructed through the variable ground of the Lambeth Group, then contingencies in the tunnelling method should be included to deal with the fullest range of ground conditions. Where this is not possible, it is necessary to appreciate the potential for variation in the Lambeth Group and design for it. Expedients can then be evaluated through risk assessment.

3   A great many tunnels and shafts have been successfully constructed through the Lambeth Group using a wide variety of methods and linings. Consequently, the hazards are generally well appreciated.

4   The presence of water-bearing sand-filled channel structures and sand, silt and gravel layers represents a construction hazard.

5   Hard bands within the group affect construction, through their abrasivity and difficulty of excavation. Their elevation, distribution and thickness need to be determined.

6   The shrink-swell behaviour of clays within the group may affect lining design and degree of overcut.

7   Selection of appropriate stiffness (E) and *in-situ* stress ratio (K_h) for tunnel and shaft lining design are problematical.

8   The behaviour of spoil comprised of more than one lithology and the effect of spoil conditioners can cause difficulties. Plant for spoil handling and treatment must be selected carefully.

9   The durability of tunnel construction materials, against the effects of potential change in the groundwater regime, needs to be assessed.

10   The presence of potentially deleterious conditions and aggressive chemicals needs to be identified.

11   There is a potential for oxygen depletion within sand-bearing strata especially those containing the clay mineral glauconite.

12   Ground loss is variable, but can be relatively low.

13   Tunnelling in free air has been successful in the upper layers, where these are generally of higher plasticity and lower permeability (eg Angel Station redevelopment).

14   The lower layers are mixed, of higher permeability, greater unpredictability and soften rapidly. Earth pressure balance machines (Jubilee Line Extension), slurry shields (Docklands Light Railway – Greenwich) and compressed air (Jubilee Line Extension – Bermondsey) have been used.

5.2   DEEP EXCAVATIONS AND CUT-AND-COVER STRUCTURES

The design of deep, single-propped or multi-propped, excavations is governed by the relative stiffness of the wall to the ground and the horizontal stress (σ_h). The retention system (wall and propping arrangement) must have sufficient capacity to resist the bending moments induced in the wall by the excavation. Fundamental to this is the selection of appropriate ground stiffness parameters and the value of *in-situ* stress ratio, K_o. Compared with the London Clay, where there are numerous case studies and the behaviour of the ground has been well established (and soil stiffness back-analysed), there are relatively few deep excavations within the Lambeth Group.

This is partly due to the depth of the group beneath the London Clay in central London and the paucity of structures within the subcrop of the Lambeth Group requiring this form of construction. Notable exceptions are the Limehouse Link Road Tunnel and stations forming the Jubilee Line Extension: Bermondsey, Canada Water and Canary Wharf.

Historically, some of London's wet docks built for handling goods were constructed within the subcrop of the Lambeth Group. Sir John Wolf Barry superintended the construction of the Surrey Dock in 1893. He described it as the most difficult job he had ever undertaken. There was so much trouble with running sand in the excavation that the dock works were not completed until 1894. Unfortunately, it is not known whether the sand referred to was the Upnor Formation or the Thanet Sand Formation.

5.2.1 Groundwater control

The presence of water-bearing strata within or immediately below the excavation usually requires dewatering both to allow excavation in the dry and to control pore pressures to prevent base heave. A review of the measures adopted within the Lambeth Group is given in Section 5.3 and also discussed by Preene and Roberts (in preparation). The measures employed for Limehouse Link road tunnel are described in Case study 5.6. Groundwater control may also be required to reduce the effect of hydrostatic uplift on a structure in the temporary case.

5.2.2 Temporary support

Excavations and retaining walls are often supported during the excavation and permanent works construction stages by temporary props or anchors at one or more levels. The need to support the wall in this way, perhaps to prevent excessive movement of the retained ground is usually balanced against the cost (monetary, time and safety to site personnel) of installing and removing temporary support. There are dangers to site personnel of moving temporary props within the excavation, which may comprise steel tubular sections 0.7 m or more in diameter and tens of metres in length. Value engineering techniques incorporating the observational method were proposed on both Limehouse Link and Bermondsey Station to enable the requirement for at least one level of temporary props to be waived. The systems employed on Limehouse Link are described in Case study 5.5.

Value engineering for the Limehouse Link road tunnel (Blyth, 1994; Glass and Powderham, 1994) **Case study 5.5**

The original design required temporary propping of the side walls by 1350 mm-diameter steel tubes at 4.2 m centres above and below the tunnel roof slab during top-down construction. These were required since there was some uncertainty over the strength and stiffness parameters for the Lambeth Group, as a result of its variability. Parameters had been based on conservative empirical relations with undrained shear strength and SPT data.

Monitoring of the props above the roof slab level showed the loads to be much lower than expected (approximately 10 per cent of the design load). Initially soft props with a predetermined gap at one end were installed and wall convergence monitored. Provided that convergence did not exceed predetermined levels, construction could proceed without propping at this level (although some props were kept available as a contingency against unacceptable movements).

A maximum convergence of 70 mm was allowed at slab soffit level. Maximum observed movement was 11 mm and a convergence less than 7 mm. The method was applied to all nine top-down construction areas, allowing 6450 t of temporary steel work to be reduced to 1550 t.

5.2.3 Excavation

Excavation for the diaphragm walls for Limehouse Link and Bermondsey Station was carried out using conventional rope grabs. Problems were experienced at Bermondsey excavating through the Lower Mottled Clays and upper part of the Upnor Formation including the pebble bed using this method, which caused buckling of the picks on the grabs. A saw-tooth arrangement overcame these difficulties. The diaphragm walls at Canary Wharf Station and the shafts at Culling Road, Pioneer Wharf, Preston's Road, Downtown Road and Old Jamaica Road were excavated using slurry trenching machines (Puller and Puller, 1993) to avoid problems excavating these materials and in some instances to provide a toe-in the underlying Chalk. Bulk excavation can normally be undertaken without undue problems using conventional plant, such as tracked backhoes, face shovels and scrapers. However, the elevation, thickness and strength of hard bands needs to be determined accurately and this information conveyed before construction since this affects the selection of excavation, drilling, boring and piling plant. Pre-drilling or excavation may be required to avoid problems.

5.2.4 Retaining system performance

Dawson *et al* (1996) report the performance of a multi-propped diaphragm wall constructed to form the box providing access to the station platforms at Bermondsey Station. The results of re-analysis of the walls before construction, using small strain stiffnesses derived from local strain measurement, enabled the contractor to modify the construction sequence and to remove a temporary prop, which increased the unsupported height of the wall. The wall was instrumented to allow the behaviour of the system to be monitored. Trigger values for wall deflections, surface settlements and prop loads were set and when these were exceeded, temporary props could be installed. Maximum measured wall deflections were less than half (11 mm) those predicted (23 mm). Subsequent back-analysis indicated that it was necessary to use a larger value for the drained stiffness of the Upnor Formation (from 300 MPa to 500 MPa) and to subdivide the Reading Formation and Woolwich Formation (previously assumed as a single clay layer) with modified drained stiffnesses from a single value of 90 MPa to 70 MPa and 500 MPa, respectively. Values of K for the Lambeth Group, determined from jack-out earth pressure cells installed in the diaphragm wall, were less than unity upon completion of the excavation.

The construction of Limehouse Link road tunnel has been described by several authors (Stevens and De Moor, 1994; Blyth, 1994; Glass and Powderham, 1994), and the use of the observational technique to allow the relaxation of propping requirements has been described in Case study 5.5. De Moor and Stevenson (1996) describe the back-analysis of the multi-propped diaphragm wall. The observed behaviour of the wall indicated that mobilised soil strains were small (wall deflections < 5 mm). The best fit for these deflections required the adoption of reduced soil stresses and high stiffnesses (Table 5.2). Measured loads in both the temporary props and roof slab and observations on site showed the effect on the behaviour was also more complex than could be anticipated during the design stage. The Limehouse Link project was one of the earliest to identify and characterise fully the various sub-units of the Lambeth Group and to recognise the significance each unit would have on design and construction.

The measurement of load on large-diameter tubular steel props installed between two parallel secant bored pile walls at Canada Water Station is described by Batten *et al* (1996). The loads measured by vibrating wire strain gauges were substantially less than the design loads and were highly susceptible to temperature changes.

Table 5.2 *Comparison of design values with those found by back-analysis for the Limehouse Link road tunnel (after De Moor and Stevenson, 1996)*

	LC	UMC	Lb	LSC	LMC	UF
Earth pressure coefficient adopted in design	1.5	2.5	1.0	2.5	2.5	2.5
Earth pressure coefficient found by back-analysis	1.1	1.9	1.0	1.9	2.5	–
Drained Young's Modulus adopted in design (MPa)	35	120	200	240	250	250
Drained Young's modulus found by back analysis (MPa)	90	360	200	400	600	–

5.2.5   Deep excavations and cut-and-cover structures: key points

1   Case studies have shown the importance of sub-dividing the Lambeth Group into its component units and assigning appropriate parameters for design to each unit.

2   The value of back-analysed *in-situ* stress is lower than the at-rest value due to the combined effects of wall installation and high stiffness of the material.

3   The values of back-analysed stiffness are substantially greater than those adopted to date in design and based on routine semi-empirical relationships.

4   Elevation, thickness, distribution and strength of hard bands need to be determined accurately and this information conveyed prior to construction. This may affect the selection of excavation, drilling, boring and piling plant. Pre-drilling or excavation may be required to avoid problems.

5   Since the units are usually water-bearing, dewatering is frequently required to control base heave and hydraulic fracture, to provide acceptable working conditions and to reduce uplift forces in the temporary case. Softening of low-plasticity clays can occur after stress relief in the mixed layer sequence.

6   The Lambeth Group as a single unit is highly cross-anisotropic, since the sub-units are thinly bedded and laminated; consequently there will be differences in vertical and horizontal permeability. Methods used to dewater excavations cannot rely on vertical drainage.

7   Local variability in water pressures, associated with wide variation in permeability, can occur at a site.

5.3   GROUNDWATER CONTROL USING DEWATERING TECHNIQUES

Underground or subsurface construction within the Lambeth Group frequently requires the implementation of measures to control groundwater within the group. Some of these measures are exclusion techniques and include: permeation grouting, ground freezing, and compressed air and, the provision of a cut-off or cofferdam. This section of the book is concerned with the application of dewatering techniques, ie those that involve the removal of water from the strata.

Groundwater control is usually required in order to:

• prevent base heave or hydraulic fracture of materials lying within or below the excavation

• provide a safe environment within which to work

- increase stability of open excavations or bores
- reduce the effects of uplift forces (buoyancy) on a structure; usually in the temporary case.

5.3.1 Hydrogeology

Permeability

The Lambeth Group, because of its variation in lithology, comprises a number of aquicludes and aquifers and as a single unit is highly cross-anisotropic in terms of permeability, having higher horizontal permeability than vertical. Anisotropy is also present within individual sub-units and this may affect the measured permeability.

Permeability of the members of the Group has been assessed/measured in several ways:

- variable or constant head tests in boreholes or piezometers
- full-scale borehole pumping tests
- empirical relations based on particle size distribution, eg Hazen's formula
- laboratory tests on samples from boreholes including oedometer, permeameter and triaxial tests.

The problems with assessing permeability using these different methods is described in CIRIA C515 *Groundwater control – design and practice* (2000). The permeability of the Lambeth Group is discussed in Section 4.17. The permeability of the various sub-units and lithological factors influencing permeability and its anisotropy are presented in Table 5 3.

Connection of any of the aquifers with overlying or underlying strata of greater permeability and with other sources of recharge, such as rivers or the sea, will considerably influence its hydrogeological characteristics (see below).

Discrete zones of potentially high permeability exist: at the base of the London Clay where the Harwich Formation may be present, as either a sand or pebble bed (eg the Blackheath Beds of south-east London); channel fill structures (infilled with material of greater permeability than the surrounding host); and, sand or gravel horizons within the Upnor Formation.

Table 5.3 *Permeability of the Lambeth Group and lithological factors influencing permeability*

Sub-unit	Measured range in permeability*	Potential behaviour	Factors influencing behaviour
Upper Shelly Clay	1×10^{-8} to 1×10^{-6}	Varies	Lamination and thin beds of sand or silt
Channel fill structures within the Reading Formation	1×10^{-3} to 1×10^{-6}	Aquifer	Size and lateral extent
Mottled clays of the Reading Formation	1×10^{-8} to 1×10^{-6}	Aquiclude	Presence and persistence of fissures
Laminated beds	1×10^{-3} to 1×10^{-6}	Varies	Degree of lamination, percentage of fine- to coarse-grained beds Fissuring in clays
Lower Shelly Clay	1×10^{-8} to 1×10^{-6}	Aquiclude	Sand laminae and thin beds of shell debris
Upnor Formation	1×10^{-3} to 1×10^{-3}	Varies (tends to aquifer)	Clay/silt content. Presence of beds of gravel or sand. Degree of cementation

* Source: Jubilee Line Extension Project

Hydrogeological scenarios in the London Basin

The Lambeth Group can present various hydrogeological scenarios, which are described below. The hydrogeology of the London Basin is often defined in terms of two aquifers: the upper aquifer comprising the River Terrace Gravels and the lower aquifer comprising the Chalk, the Thanet Sand Formation and the Upnor Formation. The two aquifers can be separated by an aquiclude comprising clay strata of the London Clay and Lambeth Group. Where the upper part of the Lambeth Group comprises permeable material and is directly overlain by the upper aquifer they may be considered together. Aquifers within the Lambeth Group can be recharged from: the Chalk; Thanet Sand Formation; River Terrace Gravel; and from rivers and the sea. Isolated lenses and permeable channel fill structures may contain connate groundwater.

Hydrogeological scenarios in the Hampshire Basin

In the Hampshire Basin the Lambeth Group is confined to a thin strip along the Sussex coast and the outcrop of the Palaeogene strata. West of Hove, clay strata tend to predominate and groundwater control may only be required where sand channel bodies are encountered or where the thin Upnor Formation is encountered.

On the Newbury Bypass, which is geographically between the Hampshire and London Basins, sand channels were encountered and dealt with by gravity drainage.

5.3.2   Methods of groundwater control using dewatering

A range of groundwater dewatering methods have been applied within the Lambeth Group. Some of the applications have been discussed elsewhere: Section 5.1 Bored tunnels and shafts, Section 5.2 Deep excavations and cut-and-cover structures, and by Preene and Roberts (in preparation).

Deep dewatering by underdrainage

Deep dewatering by underdrainage has been used successfully on a number of major projects in London including: Limehouse Link Road Tunnel (Case study 5.6), Bermondsey Station, Canada Water Station, Canary Wharf Station and a number of shaft sites on the Jubilee Line Extension (Linney and Withers, 1998). The method relies on depressurising the underlying Chalk to achieve downward flow through the Thanet Sand and Upnor Formations, thereby achieving dewatering. The method depends, therefore, on the permeability of the Chalk being greater than that of the overlying materials, and on the continuity of flow path to the well. Acidisation of the Chalk wells is known to improve yields.

Sand drains

Stratigraphically higher units in the Lambeth Group have been successfully dewatered by constructing vertical sand wicks connected to the underlying Thanet Sand Formation and Chalk. This method was carried out to dewater the Laminated beds at Limehouse Link and is described in Case Study 5.6.

Pressure relief well points

Preene and Powrie (1993) describe a project in Uxbridge, west London where well points were used to directly depressurise the Upnor Formation underlying a deep basement excavation, to provide an adequate factor of safety against base heave. The consequences of not installing and commissioning well points before excavation are also reported from a site near Windsor where base heave occurred.

Direct dewatering from well points

Well points were installed from the tunnel face and from a specially constructed pilot tunnel to dewater a sand-filled channel structure within the Reading Formation for the Victoria Line near Euston (Follenfant *et al*, 1969). This application is described in Case study 5.3.

Well points drilled from tunnels enabled the construction of a cross-passage within the Woolwich and Reading Formations in East London, thus avoiding the need for compressed air (Preene and Roberts, in preparation).

5.3.3 Gases

Dewatering or lowering of the piezometric surface may cause exposure of materials containing deleterious minerals to oxidation and the depletion of oxygen in confined atmospheres. This phenomenon has been reported on the North London Flood Relief Sewer, Lewis and Harris (in preparation). It is discussed in relation to tunnel and shafts in Section 5.1.3. Lewis and Harris describe gas monitoring of standpipes, which identified nitrogen-enriched gases and a consequent depletion of oxygen (due to oxidation reactions with minerals present in the Upnor Formation). It has also been noted in standpipes installed within the Upnor Formation for the new Hong Kong Shanghai Bank at Canary Wharf, where oxygen depletion was considered to occur as a result of the dewatering for the adjacent deep excavation for the new Jubilee Line Extension station.

5.3.4 Groundwater control using dewatering techniques: key points

1 The Lambeth Group is anisotropic and can be expected to have widely differing permeabilities both vertically and horizontally.

2 Upper or lower strata within the Lambeth Group can be in hydraulic continuity with the overlying or underlying deposits. Sources of recharge may include rivers or the sea.

3 Horizons, such as sand or silt layers within the group, may be effectively cut off from the adjacent aquifers. Storage and flow rates within these layers may be low; pressures, however, may be artesian.

4 Dewatering may cause oxidation of deleterious minerals, leading to de-oxygenation of the atmosphere and to the production of aggressive reaction products.

5 A wide range of groundwater control methods are available and their selection should be based on a detailed appraisal of the site conditions.

5.4 SLOPE STABILITY

Slope instability within the Lambeth Group occurs in a variety of forms, from mudslides, to translational slips, to rotational slips and falls (Page, in preparation). Relatively few slope failures are reported in the literature or in the BGS (formerly DoE) Landslide Database. A number of failures reported in the database are related to dissolution of the chalk and the subsequent collapse of the overlying materials.

5.4.1 Natural slopes

Much of the group lies beneath a cover of younger drift deposits and the topography is often level. However, at the edge of the basins, close to the Chalk, the topography is higher and slope instability can be a problem.

With the exception of a failure at Newhaven, coastal landslips have not been widely reported until now (Page, in preparation). The Lambeth Group outcrops on the coast at only a few localities: Bishopstone Glen/Reculver near Herne Bay in Kent; Newhaven, Shoreham, Felpham, and Chichester Harbour in Sussex; Alum Bay and Whitecliff Bay on the Isle of Wight, and Studland Bay in Dorset. Only in Kent, Newhaven and on the Isle of Wight and Dorset are these coastal slopes not influenced by the presence of younger drift.

On the Isle of Wight, slope processes affecting the Lambeth Group are similar at both Alum and Whitecliff Bays. Large, relatively steep-sided, straight gullies have developed within the Group at both localities where it is confined by the near vertically dipping Chalk and the London Clay. The gullies are being actively eroded in the winter and early spring when the steep slopes in the clay at the head of the slope become saturated. Mudslides develop, which extend lobes of debris out over the beach into the sea. During the summer, when there is little or no movement, the tongue may be eroded back towards the general line of the cliff foot (Bromhead, 1979). At Alum Bay, slope head retreat is currently threatening a number of cliff-top properties. The slopes are locally important in terms of coastal protection and shoreline management (McInnes et al, 1998).

At Newhaven, slope instability has threatened the coastal fortifications at Castle Hill (Ward, 1947). The present fort was constructed in 1864 upon an outlier of the Lambeth Group (represented by the Upnor and Woolwich Formations) and London Clay. Following heavy rain in the winter of 1942/43 a number of flat-bottomed rotational slips developed, which ran into mudflows over the top of the cliff. The slips pushed several buildings over the cliff edge and set off mines on the beach. Investigations have indicated that the slip was solely within the Woolwich Formation and that failures were probably the result of elevated pore pressures in a laminated sand and clay unit at the base of the slip. Remedial measures comprised re-profiling, the installation of rubble filled drains and clay and concrete seals to prevent recharge of the laminated sand and clay unit. Slope movements are still continuing on this slope, since wet weather in the winter of 2000/01 caused considerable further slippage.

Within 1.5 km north-east of Castle Hill, the A259 coast road runs along the strike of the Lambeth Group outlier below Rushey Hill. The road is partly in cutting and partly in cut-and-fill and had been susceptible to slope movements. Cracking and deformation of the road pavement has required frequent patching. The majority of the problems are within the Woolwich Formation. The remedial works have been carried out on a piecemeal basis and no overall slope strategy exists. More recently the remedial works have involved the installation of a sheet pile and bored pile wall, rock fill toe weighting, road realignment and slope re-profiling (1:4 slopes) as well as shallow and deep drainage.

Following harbour improvement works within the Southwick Basin at Shoreham Harbour (Ridehalgh, 1958), a significant slope failure occurred in a degraded cliff line adjacent to the A259 Brighton to Worthing coast road (Page, in preparation). The degraded cliff line is separated from the sea by a shingle spit, which has developed across the mouth of the River Adur. The intervening lagoon was subsequently developed into a harbour. The harbour improvements included dredging, to allow increased capacity colliers to serve the newly constructed power station. In early December 1957 cracks began to appear in the footpath to the coast road above the degraded cliff line; by mid-December a length of 150 m of the road was threatened by instability. During the remainder of the month the slip continued, causing the closure of the coast road, the fracture and eventual destruction of a brick tank sewer. Immediate remedial works included re-siting of a gas main, toe weighting and the re-profiling of the slope using drag lines attached to cranes working from the road above. Investigations indicated the slope failure to be controlled by the presence of a weak lignitic clay within the Woolwich Formation. The cause of the failure was attributed to removal of the toe of the slope by dredging.

Inland naturally occurring slope instability has not been widely reported. Page (in preparation) reports slope instability within a natural slope at Arundel, West Sussex. The slope has yet to be investigated, but it is thought that the failures are shallow and possibly translational in nature and were probably activated by solifluction processes. Where the same slope is encountered in the adjacent railway cutting, the slope failed in 1946. Remedial measures included a row of driven sheet piles along the toe. The adjacent A27 is also prone to ground movements where it crosses the Lambeth Group.

5.4.2   Cut slopes

The problems of forming cut slopes, primarily for the expansion of the railway, in overconsolidated soils during the nineteenth century are well known (Skempton, 1977). Although most of the cuttings around London were formed within the London Clay there were also problems in the Lambeth Group. The most notable of these is the Park Hill cutting, Croydon, which is described in Case study 5.7. This deep cutting and tunnels are important since they are now occupied by Croydon Tramlink. Other failures are known from Reading, Twyford, Yattendon and Canterbury.

Park Hill railway cutting, Croydon (Klaasen, 1883)   **Case study 5.7**

The Woolwich and Reading Beds have the reputation of being unstable, and they have fully maintained this character in the cuttings through Park Hill.

Klaasen (1883)

The section of the former Woodside and South Croydon Railway runs from north to south and extends from the Upper Addiscombe Road to Coombe Road in the south. The length of this section of the railway is 1143 m, of which 500 m is in brick-lined tunnel, with the remainder in cutting up to 26 m deep. There are three tunnels – Woodside (243 m), Park Hill (112 m) and Coombe Road (144 m) – and three cuttings: the south, central and north.

The railway was constructed between 1880 and 1885 as an alternative route to the south coast. The railway fell into disuse between 1917 and 1921 and thereafter was used only for goods and occasional special trains until September 1935, when passenger services restarted. All traffic finally ended in 1983, although the track was not removed until 1997. Three years later the cuttings and tunnels were reopened as part of the Croydon Tramlink network.

Within this section of the railway, the complete sequence from the London Clay to the Chalk is exposed in the cuttings and tunnels. The majority of the cutting, however, lies in the Lambeth Group, represented by the Upnor Formation, Upper Mottled Clay and Upper Shelly Clay. The Lower Mottled Clay (although they are probably represented by a lavender-coloured sand) are absent and the Woolwich Formation (Lower) is present as a thin bed of lignite and lignitic clay. Park Hill lies on the southern side of the London Basin and the strata dip about 1–3° to the north-west. The relationship of the strata to the cuttings and tunnels is shown in Figure 5.7.

Klaasen examined the railway cutting in 1882 and noted:

...the mottled clay stood firm at an angle of 45°, having been dressed to the same slope as the underlying sandy beds, and the neatly trimmed banks displayed the variously coloured strata with such admirable definition that the divisions in the section were seen at a glance...

However, heavy rainfall over the winter of 1882/83 (16.3 inches from October to February) caused considerable slipping of the clays in the south cutting.

...although the sand has remained comparatively undisturbed, the beds resting upon it have slipped everywhere and clay, pebbles and sand have mingled pell mell in a mass of slurry at the bottom of the cutting...

These slips completely blocked the railway and after a few days rain this was to a depth of 1.2–2.75 m. The Woolwich Formation (Upper) at the top of the cutting slipped, widening the cutting from 41 m to 54 m.

Klaasen notes:

... there can be little doubt that the angle of stability of the beds in question has by no means yet been attained, and that with a return of wet weather the movement will continue...

The Woolwich Formation (Upper Shelly Clay) in the north cutting slipped on the night of 6 October 1882. A length of the cutting, 61 m long and 10 m wide, slipped carrying with it "a hedge, wooden posts, and a cask of water ... pushing the rails and sleepers aside". In the cutting itself the (temporary contractor's) railway was lifted 2–3 feet in the course of a few hours. A previous slip in the central cutting had occurred on 27 August 1882, which covered up the line and buried eight railway wagons. The various slips nearly bankrupted the project. Additional funds had to be acquired to purchase the land at the top of the cutting affected by instability. The central cutting could not be completed in its entirety and a brick cut-and-cover tunnel was built in the base of the cutting.

Additional remedial measures are not described, but a recent examination of the slopes indicates that the slopes have been burnt. Further longer-term movements prompted the construction of brick gravity retaining walls at the base of the northern cutting within the Upper Shelly Clay.

The landslips that affected the cutting, unlike other slips in overconsolidated materials, occurred during construction. The combination of steep slopes (45°), cutting depth up to 26 m and the high incidence of rainfall contributed to the relatively quick failure.

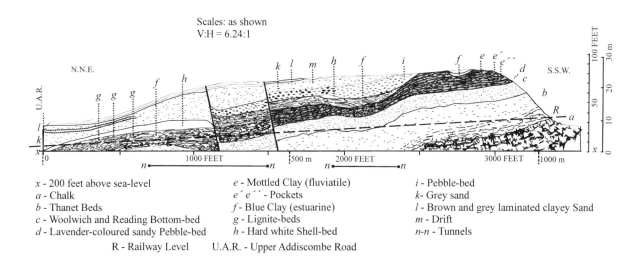

Scales: as shown
V:H = 6.24:1

x - 200 feet above sea-level
a - Chalk
b - Thanet Beds
c - Woolwich and Reading Bottom-bed
d - Lavender-coloured sandy Pebble-bed
R - Railway Level

e - Mottled Clay (fluviatile)
e´ e´´ - Pockets
f - Blue Clay (estuarine)
g - Lignite-beds
h - Hard white Shell-bed
U.A.R. - Upper Addiscombe Road

i - Pebble-bed
k- Grey sand
l - Brown and grey laminated clayey Sand
m - Drift
n-n - Tunnels

Figure 5.7 *Park Hill cutting on the former Woodside and South Croydon Railway (Klaasen, 1883)*

The stability of slopes cut through the Lambeth Group for the A34 Newbury Bypass was affected by the presence of water-bearing sand layers. They were a source of water on the slope and caused erosion of the slope. Gravel-filled slope drains, wrapped in a geotextile filter, were used to intercept these seepages. Clay units within 6 m of the surface also displayed well-developed sub-horizontal shear surfaces which, in one instance, promoted instability. A channel sand body up to 10 m deep was encountered in one cutting and was a considerable source of water (Perry *et al*, 2000).

The TRL undertook an extensive survey of earth structures forming a sample section of the motorway network in the UK (Perry, 1989). The Lambeth Group formed one of the most susceptible materials in which failures occurred. Of the cuttings within the Lambeth

Group 2.9 per cent have failed or showed signs of failure. The most common slope angle upon which failure occurred was 1:3 (v:h). Failures had typically occurred within 22 years of construction. A common result of the survey was that in overconsolidated clay soils the steepest slope was not associated with the highest incidence of failure. Cutting and also embankment slopes in overconsolidated clay deposits have a high initial strength due to the negative pore water pressures resulting from stress relief due to construction (Skempton, 1977). The rate at which this pore pressure dissipates is related to, amongst other things, slope geometry. The most rapid reductions may occur on flatter slopes, which do not drain as readily (Vaughan and Walbancke, 1973). The failure of steeper slopes is due to the interaction between the greater disturbing forces and the greater shear strength developed as a consequence of the lower pore water pressure (ie better drainage). Perry (1991) has shown that shallow failures, typical of flatter slopes, are long-term drained failures that have arisen from cracking, swelling and softening of the material closest to the surface, which under the influence of gravity driven shear strains, reduces in strength. Pore water pressures are also affected by the balance provided between precipitation, evapo-transpiration and surface runoff.

5.4.3 Embankments

There is relatively little information available on the performance of slopes made from fill derived from the Lambeth Group. This is probably because the outcrop of the group is relatively small, there are relatively few cuttings within the Lambeth Group and consequently the amount of fill material derived is small. As the earth structures that form the highway and railway network come to the end of their design life, their performance is of increasing significance for the maintainence of their serviceability.

The survey of a representative sample of the motorway network carried out by the TRL (Perry, 1989) also determined the performance and deterioration rates of earthworks (see also Andrews, 1990). Of the motorways surveyed that encountered strata of Eocene (but see following comment) and Cretaceous age, 25 per cent (ie 40.7 km) were reported as being part of the Lambeth Group. (In the survey the Reading Beds were considered of Eocene age; they are now classified as Palaeocene in age.)

As the survey was undertaken before publication of the recent work on the stratigraphy of the Group, it cannot be assumed that Reading Beds are equivalent to the Reading Formation because other formations from the Lambeth Group are likely to be present. The embankments were classified according to the origin of the fill used to form them. This was determined from construction records.

The incidence of failure within the group of embankments formed of the Lambeth Group (Reading Formation) was 7.6 per cent. Only the Gault Clay had a higher percentage of failure. The typical slope angle at which failure was occurring was 1:2 and failures occurred as a whole within 22 years of construction. The types of failure recorded were slips (translational to rotational), repaired slips, tension cracks or shrinkage cracks, settlement, water seepage and toe erosion.

Table 5.4 *Maximum slope angles allowable for embankments to restrict the percentages of failure to below 1 per cent within 22 years of construction (Perry, 1989)*

Slope height	Maximum slope angle (v:h)		
	0–2.5 m	2.5–5.0 m	> 5.0 m
Reading Formation (cohesive)	1:3	1:4	1:4
Reading Formation (non-cohesive)	1:1.75	1:1.75	1:1.75

The survey also noted that drainage ditches on the slope itself contributed significantly to reducing the number of failures. The Lambeth Group was the only geological formation that showed any distinct trend between the percentage of failure and orientation of the slope, the highest percentages of embankments showing failures faced north. In overconsolidated clays, slope failures are not always associated with the steepest slopes as described above. On the basis of the survey, Perry (1995) has suggested maximum slope angles for embankments to restrict failure to < 1 per cent within 22 years of construction (Table 5.4).

Both cut and fill slopes within Lambeth Group materials are highly susceptible to erosion due to surface water and rainfall. Consideration should be given to temporary protection if they are to remain unvegetated for any length time.

5.4.4   Slope stability: key points

1   A wide variety of forms of instability occurs within the group in both natural and cut and fill slopes.

2   Geological structure (ie position and dip of the beds) often controls the type of natural slope failure.

3   Naturally occurring slopes in southern England have usually been influenced by periglacial processes. Solifluction may have affected near-surface materials Consequently, pre-existing shear surfaces may be present and stability may be controlled by residual shear strength.

4   The presence of weak layers, such as pre-existing shear surfaces, lignitic clays, smectite rich layers, can control the position of the shear surface.

5   Pore water pressures are influenced by slope geometry, the presence of water-bearing layers, rainfall and vegetation.

6   Laminations, thin beds or permeable channel-filled structures can affect local stability by influencing the position of the shear surface, by exerting local control on pore water pressures, and by giving rise to internal erosion.

7   The high undrained strength of the Lambeth Group may permit the formation of temporary slopes steeper than those likely to be stable in the long term.

5.5   DREDGING

Dredging is important for the two principal ports located within the outcrop, at Shoreham in Sussex and the Port of London. Gunpowder has been used to loosen the calcrete outcropping in the bed of the River Thames at Limehouse (Case study 5.8). The landslip that closed the A259 in 1958 has been attributed to dredging of the Woolwich Formation within Shoreham Harbour. Here, the presence of lignitic material is used as a dredging datum.

5.6   FILL AND PAVEMENT ENGINEERING

This section considers the use and performance of the Lambeth Group as subgrade material in cuts and fills.

5.6.1   Fill materials

Due to the variability of the Lambeth Group and the relatively thin nature of each unit, fill materials derived from the group are likely to be composed of more than one unit

> **Dredging for the River Thames at Limehouse (Rennie, 1846)**　　　**Case study 5.8**
>
> Rennie describes the duricrust at the top of the Upnor Formation/Lower Mottled Clay that forms the bed of the river as follows:
>
> > ...(it) has been hitherto a great detriment to steam vessels navigating the above [Limehouse] Reach at low water, and measures are in progress to remove the same by means of dredging-engines, which have been in operation for seven or eight months; great difficulty is found in breaking through the strata or crust with the iron buckets attached to the engines, which have been carried away on many occasions, although steel pointed. Gunpowder is occasionally resorted to break up the strata after which it is easily removed...
>
> Upstream, the same duricrust was encountered not only in the Thames Tunnel but also the Rotherhithe Tunnel. Barrow (1905) describes:
>
> > ...the engineers came on the taper end of a fine hard sandstone which slowly thickened to about three feet. This material is commonly known as Sarsen... after a considerable length had been cut through, the Sarsen began to contain small scattered flint pebbles. These became larger and more numerous till the rock finally passed into puddingstone. It did not retain this character further on; patches only were cemented, the rest was loose, thus becoming the normal pebble bed...
>
> This duricrust was encountered within the excavations for Canada Water Station on the Jubilee Line Extension (Page and Skipper, 2000 – see Figure 4.4).

and more than one lithology. Acceptance criteria should be taken into account at the planning, investigation and construction stages.

The Lambeth Group were encountered on the Newbury Bypass in three cuttings between 12 m and 18 m deep where they comprised a sequence of firm to very stiff mottled clays (Reading Formation) and silty sands. The Lambeth Group proved to be a good source of good fill material for embankments and landscaping once in an acceptable condition. However, the moderately low plasticity clays and silty sands proved highly sensitive to changes in moisture content.

5.6.2　　Subgrade

The selection of an appropriate CBR for a Lambeth Group subgrade should consider the elevation of the groundwater level, site drainage, proximity to sand layers and trafficking. Since the Lambeth Group is predominantly cohesive, subgrades will usually require protection and/or replacement.

As the moderately low-plasticity clays and silty sands proved highly sensitive to changes in moisture content, pavement design on the Newbury Bypass for the very stiff mottled clays of the Reading Formation and silty sands of the Lambeth Group was based upon a subgrade CBR < 2 per cent. A 600 mm layer of crushed concrete capping, used as subgrade replacement, performed well during construction.

Treatment of Chalk solution features (Rhodes and Marychurch, 1998)   Case study 5.9

Rhodes and Marychurch (1998) describe the treatment of some sites in southern England affected by solution of the Chalk underlying the Lambeth Group: at Chieveley in Berkshire for a road improvement scheme, and at site near Newbury for a housing development.

At Chieveley the Lambeth Group comprised interbedded sands and clays overlying the Chalk in an area of known chalk dissolution. The ground investigation consisted of trial pits, boreholes, window sampling and dynamic probing. These exploratory holes were positioned at every structure and at 50 m intervals along the proposed carriageway and slip roads. Where solution features were encountered, their lateral and vertical extent was investigated. It was considered that this investigation would enable identification of the type, nature and frequency of solution features, such that mitigating measures could be designed before construction works started. The solution features were considered to be a hazard that had the potential to give rise to long-term settlements and reduced bearing capacity. The investigations revealed features from pipes as narrow as 500 mm to as wide as 20 m in diameter. Deeper solution features were encountered where there was a significant thickness of granular Lambeth Group overlying the Chalk. The features were infilled with highly variable material comprising firm to stiff clays, medium dense sand and gravel and mixtures of the two.

Several design options were prepared in advance of construction according to the type and size of solution feature encountered. Beneath roads, small features < 1 m diameter were treated using either a concrete cap or placing a geo-grid-reinforced granular blanket to span the features should collapse of the infill occur. Larger features within granular fill were to be compacted using dynamic compaction or vibro-displacement and the subsequent depression infilled with granular fill incorporating geo-grid reinforcement. Large features with soft cohesive infill were to be treated using vibro-replacement forming stone columns within the fill and penetrating into the Chalk. The stone columns improve bearing capacity of the infill prior to the geo-grid-reinforced granular mattress being constructed. Close to structures and services, where vibro columns would not be appropriate the features were capped with concrete, either reinforced or unreinforced. Beneath embankments, the solution features would give rise to settlements greater than those on Chalk and a geo-grid reinforced granular blanket was designed to limit deflection of the carriageway to less than 1 per cent, should collapse of the features infilled with sand and gravel occur. Elsewhere, where the feature was infilled with cohesive material, use was made of the combination of: dynamic compaction or vibro replacement, with capping of the neck of the void; excavation and filling of smaller features; and concrete capping.

The adopted treatment for bridge foundations was dependent on the type and size of the solution feature. For small pipes of less than 1 m in diameter, excavation of the infill and replacement with structural fill or mass concrete was considered appropriate, as this allowed rapid treatment without delaying the contract. Where larger features were present, reinforced concrete rafts were designed to span over the features and transfer the load on to the Chalk. For particularly wide solution features (> 8 m), the use of a capping slab alone was precluded by the width of the slab required to achieve the bearing capacity from the surrounding Chalk. One option was to pile, with the piles located no closer than two pile diameters from the feature, so as to avoid interacting with the feature. This allowed the necessary bearing capacity to be achieved without extending the footprint of the structure too far beyond the solution feature.

5.6.4   Fill and pavement engineering: key points

1   There is very little information on the performance of the Lambeth Group materials in earthworks.

2   The behaviour of the earthwork materials of the Lambeth Group would be expected to depend on the proportion of lithologies present. Fill would be anticipated to comprise a mixture of the lithologies at source. Fine-grained lithologies are generally dominant.

3   Fine-grained lithologies are known to be particularly sensitive to water. Rapid softening occurs because of interbedding *in situ* and mixing during placement.

4   Alternative engineering solutions should be developed in areas prone to chalk dissolution.

5.7   PILED FOUNDATIONS

Over the past 50 years many sites, especially within central London, have been redeveloped. With the pressure for available sites and advances in construction techniques, the structures have become progressively larger, often requiring complex deep foundations, which have taken them below the drift cover and the overlying London Clay. Furthermore, with the spread of development along the East Thames corridor, where the subcrop of the Lambeth Group is more extensive, foundation design in the Lambeth Group is becoming increasingly relevant.

There are, however, many structures founded on piles within the Lambeth Group, although there are relatively few published data on pile behaviour. Appendix 3 lists major case studies on pile behaviour. The case studies are biased towards major developments within London, particularly those within the London Docklands Development Area.

5.7.1   Pile selection and design considerations

The selection and performance of piled foundations reflects the variable lithology of the Lambeth Group and the problems in obtaining and interpreting adequate information on the group. A wide variety of pile types has been used including: large-diameter bored piles, continuous flight auger (CFA) piles, driven steel tubes, driven pre-cast and hand-dug piles, under-reamed piles constructed in the top of the Lambeth Group, and base grouted piles founded in the top of the underlying Thanet Sand Formation.

An example of the selection of the type of piled foundation being influenced by the quality of the information derived from the ground investigation is provided by the Shell Centre. Williams (1957), Measor and Williams (1958) and Skempton and Henkel (1957) recognised the difficulty of determining the undrained shear strength of the group within central London for pile design for the Shell Building and that values derived from samples taken from undisturbed driven U100 tubes were not representative of the strength of the material. Williams (1957) notes that it is much harder than the London Clay and that it took 200 blows of the drive hammer to obtain a U100 sample. The foundations were designed as cast in place piles with under-reamed bases, the location of which was influenced by the presence of water-bearing silty sand. The Lambeth Group offered reduced pile settlements compared to the London Clay, but investigations revealed that the sand unit at the top of the Upper Mottled Clay was under artesian pressure of about 12 m, which could destabilise the unlined bore. The piles were stopped short of the Lambeth Group and founded in the London Clay.

Subsequently, investigations for the piled foundations for the Central YMCA (Tottenham Court Road) incorporated a 1 m-diameter trial pile shaft, which was subsequently logged and plate bearing tests carried out (St John, 1975). No water-bearing strata or sand channels were encountered in the trial pile, but their presence over the remainder of the site could not be discounted. The plate bearing tests confirmed the high stiffness and bearing capacity of the mottled clay – a value of 1 MPa was assigned as allowable bearing stress in the final design. The piles were designed as 2 m-diameter bored cast *in-situ* piles with 5 m-diameter under-reams in the Clay to carry a column load of around 25 MN.

The presence or absence of sand-filled channel structures within the Upper Mottled Clay has also influenced the selection of piles and their founding level at No 1 Embankment Place. The designers were deterred from founding in the Upper Mottled Clay by the presence of the sand, which could destabilise the bore; foundation solutions used under-reams in the London Clay instead. Even where ground investigation information suggested that water-bearing strata were absent, their presence in other areas of the site could not be discounted and there was significant risk associated with the adoption of open bored piling.

The largest bored piles formed to date within the Lambeth Group are those for the foundations of Westminster Station on the JLE. The foundations for this structure also incorporate those for the new parliamentary building on the Embankment. The 3 m-diameter piles were designed to carry 38 MN in skin friction only and to resist heave forces generated from the excavation of a 38 m-deep box. The piles were founded within the calcrete of the Lower Mottled Clay. The design was hampered by the fact that there were no reliable strength data on the Lambeth Group; the piles were designed using an effective stress approach.

The piled foundations for the Stratford Market Depot building on the Jubilee Line Extension were originally designed to take a contribution of load in end bearing from a sand unit within the Laminated beds. However, investigations indicated that the sand unit was not continuous across the site and the contractor's choice of the CFA piling technique meant that the unit could not be readily identified during boring. The contractor chose to redesign the piles as friction piles to consistent dimensions.

Case study 5.9 describes the use of a piled foundation solution for road bridge piers in an area prone to Chalk solution features. Where wide solution features were encountered (> 8 m wide) piles were installed within the surrounding Chalk no closer than two pile diameters to avoid interaction with the feature.

5.7.2   Pile construction

The problems of constructing open bores within the upper part of the Lambeth Group were fully appreciated during the design of foundations for the Shell Centre, No 1 Embankment Place and the Central YMCA, as described above. The stability of open bores was also examined by Steger and Derbyshire (1975) who report a trial pile at Euston Square remaining stable for a period of few hours, sufficient for the placement of concrete. Despite this, the piles were constructed under bentonite to reduce the risk of instability, base disturbance, base heave, problems due to delays in concreting and to allow the placement of concrete via a tremie providing better quality concrete than free-fall concreting. Piles at the adjacent British Library at Euston (Figure 5.8) were bored dry through the Lambeth Group (O'Riordan, 1982) without apparent problems.

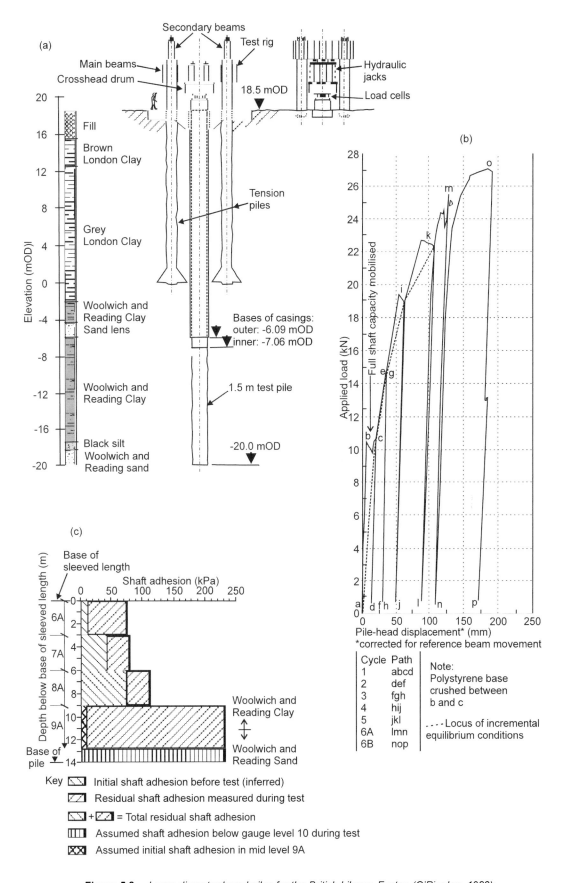

Figure 5.8 *Large-diameter bored piles for the British Library, Euston (O'Riordan, 1982):*
(a) pile test arrangement and ground conditions, (b) load–displacement curve,
(c) distribution of shaft resistance

A 1.2 m-diameter trial pile for the Canary Wharf Development remained stable through the clays of the Woolwich Formation and Lower Mottled Clay, although instability occurred at the base of the Upnor Formation. Water was added in an attempt to balance the groundwater pressure but was lost as the Thanet Sand Formation was penetrated. Subsequent piles were constructed under bentonite (Troughton, 1992).

Where bored or CFA piles are constructed through overlying drift materials, such as River Terrace Gravel, casing is sealed into the underlying clay, which is usually used to prevent ingress of water and soil.

Open-ended driven steel tubular piles were constructed to form the foundations to over-water structures within the Canary Wharf development (Gaba, 1989). Three types of hydraulic hammer were examined during driving trials. The pile driving records are given in Figure 5.9. The piles were founded in the Thanet Sand Formation.

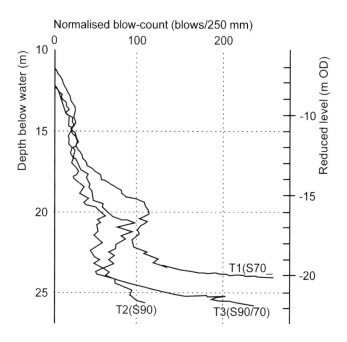

Figure 5.9   *Blowcounts when driving tubular steel piles at Canary Wharf (Gaba, 1989)*

Pre-cast concrete piles (350 mm square) for the Westferry Circus car park were driven to a minimum set of 100 blows for 250 mm. However, a number of piles refused above the specified minimum elevation of -14 m OD because of the presence of an impersistent limestone horizon (duricrust below the Mid Lambeth Group hiatus). Load tests showed that the piles were acceptable, because of their high end-bearing resistance (Troughton, 1992). The duricrust has been used elsewhere to found structures; where CFA piles and diaphragm walls met refusal as in Figure 5.10 (Troughton 1992) and, where present beneath the South Quay Plaza Phase 2 (Solera, 1998).

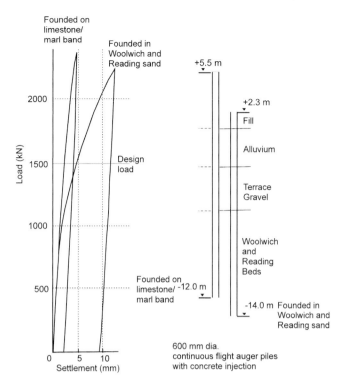

Figure 5.10 *Canary Wharf CFA piles founded on calcrete (duricrust) and in the Upnor Formation (Troughton, 1992)*

5.7.3   Pile performance and design

Many types of pile have been constructed within the Lambeth Group. Many of the piles pass through overlying deposits in addition to the Lambeth Group and some are founded in the underlying dense Thanet Sand Formation. Investigators have attempted to gain more information on the performance of the pile, in terms of shaft and base loads, by performing load tests, with, for example, frictionless sleeving along the upper part of the pile through the overlying materials, instrumentation through extensometers and strain gauges, tension load tests or the provision of a soft polystyrene inclusion at the pile base. Wherever possible, shaft friction, base resistance and design parameters have been back-analysed and provided in Appendix 3, using the information on *in-situ* effective stress conditions at the time of testing.

Careful interpretation of instrumentation data allowed O'Riordan (1982) to measure the shaft friction developed on a large-diameter bored pile through the Upper Mottled Clay as shown on Figure 5.8(c). Unit shaft friction in the Upper Mottled Clay ranged between f_s = 75 and 113 kPa. This corresponds to relatively low values of

$$\alpha = 0.36 \text{ to } 0.4$$

where:

$$Q_s = \pi.D.L_s.f_s$$

and

$$f_s = \alpha.c_u$$

where:

D = pile diameter

L_s = embedded shaft length in clay

c_u = undrained shear strength from undrained triaxial tests on 102 mm-diameter
     samples = 200–280 kPa

Much higher values of $\alpha = 0.8$ ($c_u = 100$ kPa, ie unit shaft friction, $f_s = 80$ kPa) were back-analysed by Chapman *et al* (1999) for base grouted piles at Canary Wharf, though this was attributed to the cemented pebble layer (duricrust) at the top of the Lower Mottled Clay/Upnor Formation. Lower values of $\alpha = 0.4$ were applied in design to account for the absence of this material in other areas over the site. This corresponds to a shaft friction $f_s = 40$ kPa. It should be noted that back-figured α values are highly dependent on the chosen c_u design line and the degree of conservatism adopted in cases of wide scatter in c_u results. f_s values are dependent on construction method.

O'Riordan's analysis showed that the unit shaft friction in the Upnor Formation was double that in the overlying clays at 230 kPa. Lower values were reported by Yeats and O'Riordan (1989), Troughton and Platis (1989) and Chapman *et al* (1999), due to the lower effective stress conditions at these sites. K values range between 0.47 (O'Riordan, 1982) and 1.05 (Chapman *et al*, 1999) where:

$$Q_s = \pi.D.L_s.\sigma_v'.K.\tan\varphi'$$

and

σ_v' = average free-field vertical effective stress

φ' = peak internal angle of friction (33° to 35°).

Pile base capacity in the clays of the Lambeth Group is relatively small. Most designers use the standard expression

$$Q_b = \frac{1}{4}.\pi.D^2.N_c.c_u$$

where

$N_c = 9$.

There are no published load test data for piles founded in the clay within the Lambeth Group. Piles founded in the underlying Upnor Formation reached base resistances between 7 and 14 MPa, or N_q values ranging between 14 and 42 where:

$$Q_b = \frac{1}{4}.\pi.D^2.N_q.\sigma_v'$$

A base resistance of 11.7 MPa ($N_q = 62$) was deduced from the CFA piles founded on the calcrete band (duricrust), see Figure 5.11 (Solera, 1998). A stiffer load settlement response is recorded by Troughton for piles founded on the calcrete than on the underlying Upnor Formation (Figure 5.10).

Axial and lateral load tests were conducted on the driven tubular steel piles described by Gaba (1989) as shown on Figure 5.12.

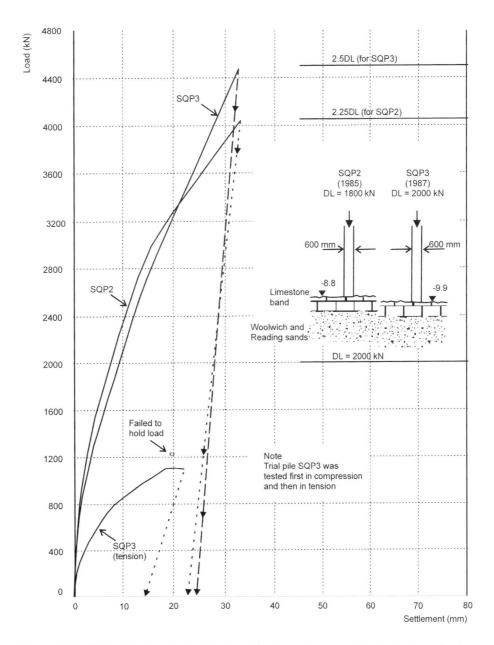

Figure 5.11 *Pile load test results for CFA piles in tension and compression founded on calcrete (duricrust) at South Quay Plaza, London Docklands (Solera, 1998)*

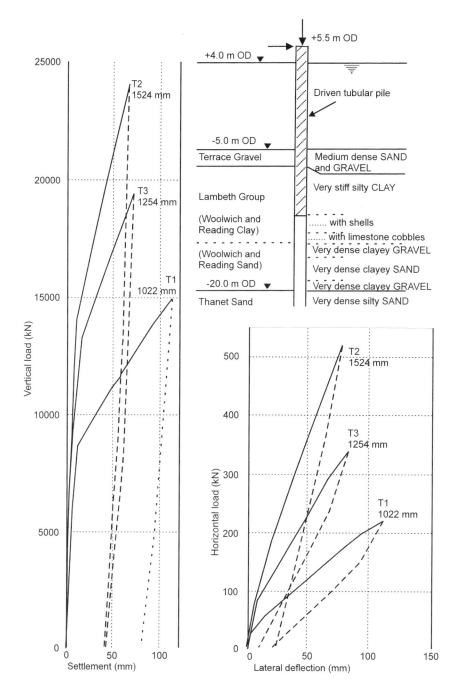

Figure 5.12 *Summary of axial and lateral load tests on driven tubular piles at Canary Wharf (Gaba, 1989)*

5.7.4   Piled foundations: key points

1   Because of the heterogeneity of the Lambeth Group and the presence of potential water-bearing strata, the general philosophy for piling has been to avoid the group and either found above in the overlying London Clay, or below in the Thanet Sand Formation or Chalk.

2   The design of piles has been carried out using total stresses (alpha method: Skempton, 1959) or effective stresses (beta method: Burland, 1973). The problems of using the alpha method are in accurately determining the value of undrained shear strength either directly or from empirical relations with SPTs.

3   The presence of water-bearing strata may dictate the pile length, its type and the construction methods adopted. A ground investigation may not reveal their presence across the whole site.

4   Piles have been designed to take a proportion of the vertical load in end bearing on layers of hard clay, on sand or on duricrust.

5   The continuity of strata across a site may influence the design of piles that derive a proportion of their resistance from end bearing in the strata. The potential for its absence should be evaluated and expedients considered during design.

6   The presence, elevation, thickness and strength of hard bands that may form an obstruction to some forms of piling or alternatively may offer a potential foundation solution, should be established.

7   The presence of Chalk solution features beneath the Lambeth Group may necessitate alternative piling arrangements.

8   There is a paucity of published pile load test data on the Lambeth Group, other than for major projects in London.

5.8   SHALLOW FOUNDATIONS

Shallow foundation design and construction is governed by the following factors:

- adequate bearing capacity
- foundation movement either due to applied loads or in the long-term due to factors, such as the presence of shrinkable or swelling clays, proximity to vegetation and fluctuating groundwater levels
- potential construction problems in forming these foundations eg groundwater, difficult excavation, hard ground etc.

Because of the variable lithology, the Lambeth Group offers a range of foundation conditions and problems.

5.8.1   Assessment of adequate bearing capacity

In the UK shallow foundation design is based on the assessment of undrained shear strength of clays or density of granular material. This is routinely obtained from a visual estimation of strength or penetrometer tests carried out in trial pits, or from SPTs. The data are used to determine adequate bearing pressures, founding levels and likely settlement for the applied loads. The problems inherent in assessing design parameters from these tests in the Lambeth Group are described in Section 6.9.

The proposed development may be constrained by areas of inadequate bearing capacity. Rhodes and Marychurch (1998) describe a site near Newbury comprising approximately 10 m of Lambeth Group underlain by the Chalk where several chalk solution features were present at the surface as shallow circular depressions. Following investigation of these features it was concluded that the proposed development could not be sited clear of them. Structures were located in areas of potentially lower risk and the associated roads and infrastructure located in higher-risk areas. Foundations for houses were designed as stiff reinforced rafts, able to span 3 m in the event of a collapse within the footprint of the structure and to cantilever 1.5 m at the edges.

5.8.2   Foundation behaviour

There are very few published data on the performance of shallow foundations on the Lambeth Group, and presumably the long-term performance of these foundations is not a major problem. Morton and Au (1974) report foundation settlements for two structures founded on the Lambeth Group, one a raft in Croydon the other piled near the base of this unit. Settlement for both structures was approximately 50 mm. Morton and Au indicated that these settlements were approximately half those for similar structures founded on the London Clay.

The presence of reactive clay minerals results in lithologies with shrink/swell potential. There are few, though significant, incidents where damage to structures founded on shallow foundations has occurred due to their location on the Lambeth Group (BRE database). There are fewer incidents of movement resulting in damage since the outcrop of the Lambeth Group, by comparison to the London Clay and Gault Clay, is much smaller. Chandler *et al* (1992) describe the foundation problem to a house founded on the Lambeth Group on mottled clay (Case study 5.10).

The Lambeth Group contains clays exhibiting a wide range in plasticity (Section 4.7). In clays with high plasticity, it is reasonable to expect that foundation problems similar to those in the London Clay could occur and foundation design should consider the presence of clays with high shrink/swell potential due to seasonal changes in the groundwater regime, leaking drains or tree root desiccation. Investigations should be appropriately designed.

Damage to a house constructed on the Lambeth Group in Harrow (Chandler *et al*, 1992)   **Case study 5.10**

Chandler *et al* (1992) use the results from the assessment of soil suctions using the filter paper method to assess the cause of damage to a house constructed in 1977–78. The site is underlain by 6 m of clay whose plasticity reduces with depth and which overlies dense sand. Prior to construction of the house a considerable number of trees, some as much as 16 m in height, had been removed.

An investigation was carried out in December 1987 to examine the cause of damage to the building, thought to be the consequence of heave. Two borings, from which U100 samples were obtained, both clearly established that at shallow depths the soil suctions were near the anticipated equilibrium values and, at least in Borehole 1, the natural water content was well above the plastic limit. Considerable quantities of water were encountered in shallow trial pits. However, the measured suctions increased rapidly below 2 m, with values at 6 m depth approaching 1000 kPa.

These high suctions are no doubt in part due to the former presence of trees, although the suctions may be influenced to some extent by the presence of the underlying sand, perhaps due to underdrainage and desaturation. This suggestion is supported by the observation that water was not encountered in the sand in either boring, and nor is there any indication in the filter paper test results of a reduction in suction in the clay immediately above the sand.

While, the ground water conditions in this case are unusual, it is an important example in that it demonstrates that high suctions can remain in the ground for a significant time, even though there is ample water at shallow depths. This carries the implication that significant ground swelling could occur in the future at this site, and that great care would be required in assessing the appropriate remedial works.

The presence of sand laminae or beds within close proximity to a foundation in clay may potentially cause problems. If found to be water-bearing they may cause softening of the foundation and they may also make construction of foundation excavations difficult. If found dry, consideration should be given to the likelihood that they could become saturated and cause the clay to swell, perhaps due to seasonal effects, a change in groundwater level or leaking drains (which could also promote subsidence through the removal of fines). This will affect the long-term performance of the foundation.

Where the Lambeth Group directly overlies the Chalk then the strata may be susceptible to subsidence due to the formation of sinkholes or dolines in the Chalk. This form of subsidence may be large and occur rapidly as voids created in the Lambeth Group migrate to the surface. The process acts under gravity but may be exacerbated by groundwater or leaking drains/water supply causing the removal of fines; it may be triggered by excavations. Areas prone to this form of subsidence have been identified by Edmunds (1983) and McDowell (1989).

5.8.3   Shallow foundations: key points

1   Clay lithologies containing clay minerals with high cation exchange capacity have the potential for large volume change and potentially damaging movements. Movements can be exacerbated by the presence of vegetation (tree roots), leaking drains, a high water table etc.

2   The presence of water-bearing sand laminae/beds within predominantly clay lithologies may make foundation construction difficult and may provide a source of water which may reduce bearing capacity or affect long-term foundation behaviour.

3   The presence of solution features within the Chalk underlying the Lambeth Group may lead to the development of sinkholes or dolines. In areas prone to this phenomenon, investigations should be geared to locating the presence and extent of these features. Void migration in the overlying strata may be promoted by groundwater movement, including the presence of leaking drains.

6 Ground investigation

A ground investigation in the Lambeth Group always has to be tailored to suit the scale of the project, the type of construction that is proposed and the design methods that it is envisaged will be used. The prime objective of any investigation has to be to establish the local stratigraphy – which units are present, their thickness, boundary elevations and variability across the site – and, from this, to develop a ground model. Additional objectives will, in most cases, be to determine the groundwater conditions and the likelihood of encountering any of the geological hazards discussed in Chapter 3. The design parameters to be determined depend on whether or not performance data exist for the proposed construction type in these ground conditions and have been linked to *in-situ* or laboratory index tests, such as SPT. If so, the index tests need to be carried out using the same methods as those used to establish that link. *In-situ* testing and the recovery of high quality samples for laboratory testing may be justified where engineering properties, as opposed to design parameters, of individual units are required.

The ground investigation should be designed taking into account the lithological variation within the Lambeth Group, its particular depositional environment and the post-depositional processes to which it has been subjected.

6.1 DESK STUDY

As in any ground investigation, the first step should be a desk study in which the location of the site within its depositional basin, London or Hampshire, should be established. The local geological sheet and memoir should be consulted, together with the local register of important geological sites, for information on any local exposures. Exposures should be inspected, logged and photographed. Available borehole logs and well records should be studied and an attempt made to develop tentative geological sections, which can be used to guide the proposed site investigation. Case histories of similar work in the Lambeth Group should be sought and studied to identify potential problems.

Information on groundwater conditions should be obtained, including details of local abstractions and dewatering schemes.

6.2 STRATIGRAPHY AND GROUNDWATER CONDITIONS

6.2.1 Stratigraphy

An important breakthrough in understanding the Lambeth Group has been the elucidation of the stratigraphy and the recognition of the various internal members that comprise each Formation. The lithologies of the Lambeth Group are quite distinctive and with careful sampling and logging it is possible to establish the local stratigraphy. Methods to establish the local stratigraphy depend on the depth at which the Lambeth Group exists. They should enable continuous exposures (in trial pit, shaft or natural exposure) or continuous cores to be examined. The lithology is such that recovery of tube samples cannot be relied upon and a full profile is unlikely to be obtained. Developments in rotary coring techniques, in particular the introduction of triple tube coring with semi-rigid plastic liners (see Section 6.5), have made total volume coring in the Lambeth Group feasible, although difficulties remain in obtaining samples in the pebble beds. It is these techniques that have contributed to the improved understanding of the geology of the Lambeth Group.

Both descriptive (ground investigation) and interpretative (geological) logs should be prepared, together with photographic records of exposures or cores. Particular care should be taken with the:

- elevation, thickness, and type of hard bands, eg whether marine limestone or calcrete duricrust

- identification and distribution of pyrite or gypsum.

Identification of individual units within the Lambeth Group should be possible on the basis of the descriptions presented in Tables 4.2 and 4.3 and the core and exposure photographs contained in Appendix 2. Facies of the Reading Formation are distinguishable on the basis of their ochreous mottling, as a result of subaerial weathering, which contrasts with the greys of the shallow marine sediments of the Woolwich Formation.

The difficulties posed by the rapid vertical and lateral variability in stratigraphy are emphasised in Figure 2.5 which shows the different units that might be encountered in two adjacent boreholes. Difficulties also arise in identifying emergent and bioturbated boundaries that are gradational, such as between the Lower Mottled Clay and Lower Shelly Clay.

Page (1994) and Page and Skipper (2000) suggest that successful correlation between boreholes relies in the accurate identification of sequence boundaries, such as those at the base and top of the Group and at the mid-Lambeth Group hiatus. The base of the Reading Formation is not a reliable marker horizon as it is frequently diachronous and probably only represents the depth of pedogenesis. Care has to be taken in the selection of a datum for plotting results of *in-situ* or laboratory tests. For a transgressive sequence (eg Upnor Formation) the base of the unit may be appropriate, whereas to investigate the effects of weathering, the ground surface may be appropriate. Care needs to be taken in logging the samples. Confusion has arisen in the past because limestone described on borehole logs has been assumed to be of marine origin and, therefore, in the Woolwich Formations, whereas it could equally well have been a calcrete of pedogenic origin within the Reading Formation. Identifying the top of the Reading Formation helps to avoid this confusion.

The importance of identifying the presence of channel deposits, containing sands that may be laminated and cross-bedded, and may cut through the different formations, cannot be overemphasised.

6.2.2 Groundwater conditions

Groundwater conditions are likely to be complex in the London area, involving the effects of previous under-drainage and rising groundwater and with the possibility of perched water tables. The installation of sealed piezometers at different elevations and their long-term monitoring are likely to be essential. The potential effects of local extractions or dewatering for other projects need to be carefully considered.

It should be recalled that groundwater seepages will be obscured during rotary drilling. This may warrant the construction of an adjacent borehole to identify water strikes.

6.3 *IN-SITU* TESTING

6.3.1 Standard penetration testing (SPT)

The standard penetration test (SPT) has been widely used in ground investigations in the Lambeth Group. Examples are presented in Figures 4.68 to 4.72. These generally show a wide scatter, reflecting in part the natural variability in the materials, in particular the presence of hard layers, but possibly influenced by details of the test. Blow counts are often high, requiring extrapolation to SPT N values above 50.

It is important in carrying out the test to adhere to the guidelines set out in CIRIA Report 143 (Clayton, 1995) and in BS 1377 Part 9:1990, to ensure that water balance is maintained when penetrating sand layers and that the base of the borehole is always properly cleaned. It is likely that only locally established correlations will be of use.

Empirical correlations between SPT N values and design parameters have not been firmly established for units of the Lambeth Group.

6.3.2 Cone penetration testing (CPT)

An example of data from cone penetration tests in the Lambeth Group at Stratford has been presented in Figure 4.73 and it demonstrates that the different units can be distinguished on the basis of their particular q_c and f_s signatures. Again, difficulties arise in penetrating hard layers and a drilling rig is often required to allow the cone to be advanced downhole. Cone penetration testing is likely to be more valuable when the Lambeth Group is encountered at shallow depths.

Correlations between engineering properties and design parameters for the Lambeth Group and CPT parameters have not yet been established.

6.3.3 Pressuremeter testing

Menard pressuremeter testing was used in the investigation for the Fleet Line (now the Jubilee Line) in 1977. Self-boring pressuremeter testing has been used with some success in ground investigations in the Lambeth Group, eg Limehouse Link, CTRL, JLE, Crossrail, Sizewell and Angel Station, but difficulties have arisen because of the presence of hard strata and interbedding within the test pocket.

Pressuremeter test depths should be selected on the basis of the inspection of continuous rotary cores from adjacent boreholes. Layers in the pebble beds containing flint gravel, and limestone bands in the Lower Shelly Clay and duricrusts in the Lower Mottled Clay should be avoided because of the difficulties of self boring and the risk of damage to the membrane. Gravels and shells also disturb the walls of the test pocket and increase the risk of membrane damage. The self-boring pressuremeter needs to be used in conjunction with a drilling rig to clear obstructions when advancing to the next test location. In the hard strata, it may be beneficial to use the weak rock pressuremeter/ high-pressure dilatometer.

6.3.4 *In-situ* plate testing

Plate testing, either at the base of trial pits, shafts or boreholes, using techniques established by Marsland (1971), would appear to have an important role to play in ground investigation in the Lambeth Group for the following reasons.

1 The Lambeth Group is layered at various scales, making the measurement and selection of parameters for individual layers difficult. Parameters defining an integrated response of the layered sequence are often required and these can be determined from a properly interpreted large-diameter plate test.

2 The potential effects of stress relief and sampling are particularly severe in the soils making up the group and these effects can be largely avoided in a carefully excavated and prepared pit or borehole.

Plate loading tests in the Lambeth Group were undertaken to assess its suitability for founding piles, which were to support the main tower structure of the YMCA (St John, 1975). The ground conditions at the site of the YMCA near Tottenham Court Road Underground Station are shown in Figure 6.1. The log was made from the visual inspection of the sides of a 1 m-diameter shaft. The base of the London Clay is about 26 m below ground level, at an elevation of approximately -0.3 m OD.

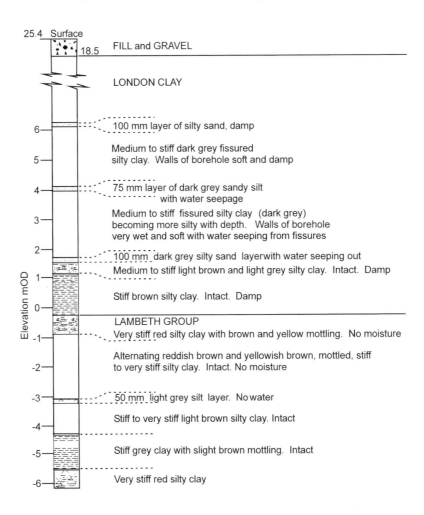

Figure 6.1 *Borehole log, YMCA, Tottenham Court Road, London*

From interpretations made for the nearby Crossrail site investigation, the Lambeth Group underlying the London Clay is believed to comprise a thick sequence of Upper Mottled Clay.

Five tests were carried out and details of each are summarised in Table 6.1. The procedures and equipment are described by Marsland (1971). In tests A3, A4 and A5, a load cycle was performed over a range of up to half the expected ultimate load before loading the plate to failure under a constant rate of penetration of 2.5 mm/minute. A typical load cycle is shown in Figure 6.2. No load cycles were carried out in tests B1 and B2.

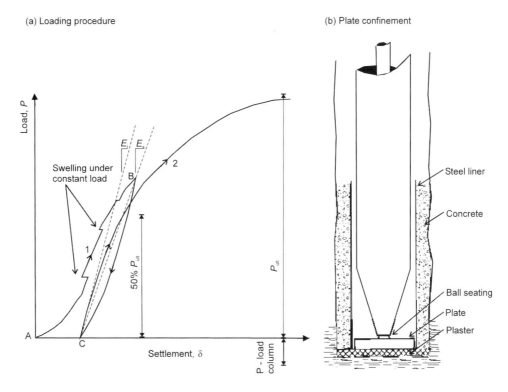

(a) Loading procedure

(b) Plate confinement

Figure 6.2 *Loading procedure and details of plate confinement for plate loading tests at YMCA, Tottenham Court Road*

The mode of failure in tests B1 and B2 was thought to be confined at the base of a borehole more than 25 m below ground level. Confinement was achieved by embedding the plate at the bottom of a heavy gauge concrete pipe, concreted over its 1.83 m length, see Figure 6.2. The mode of failure in tests A3, A4 and A5 was believed to be only partially confined as the diameter of the plate was smaller than the diameter of the hole and no confining pipe was used in A3 and A4, and although used in A5, it was not entirely successful.

The undrained strength of the clay has been interpreted from each test by making the assumption that all the tests were confined with the end-bearing being given by $P_{ULT} = 9.C_u$. The assumption that the tests were confined may be conservative (ie underestimate the undrained strength) for tests A3, A4 and A5.

Values of Young's modulus have been calculated for each test from the semi-empirical formula:

$$E = (p/\delta).(\pi/4).(1-\mu^2). f(z/D)$$

where

p = load/plate area

δ = settlement/plate diameter

$\mu = 0.5$

$f(z/D) = 0.87$, a depth factor (Burland, 1969).

The interpreted strength and stiffness for each test is summarised in Table 6.1, where quoted secant modulus is taken between zero load and half the ultimate load.

Table 6.1   *Results of plate load tests in Lambeth Group, YMCA, Tottenham Court Road, London*

Test	Plate diameter (mm)	Geological description	Elevation (m OD)	Settlement at failure (mm)	P_{ULT} (kN)	Ultimate bearing pressure (MPa)	Inferred c_u (kPa)	Inferred E_{sec} (MPa)
B1	560 confined	Very stiff clay reddish brown and yellowish brown mottling (UMC)	-2.4	1.3	> 3 700	> 15	> 1 671	242
B2	560 confined	Stiff grey clay with slight brown mottling (UMC)	-5.4	1.3	2 600	10.6	1 174	275
A3	860 unconfined	Very stiff clay reddish brown and yellowish brown mottling (UMC)	-2.4	1.9	> 1 720	> 3.0	>329	258
A4	560 unconfined	Stiff to very stiff light brown silty clay (UMC)	-3.9	1.6	1 880	7.6	849	181
A5	560 probably unconfined	Stiff grey clay with slight brown mottling (UMC)	-5.4	0.8	1 880	7.6	849	167

Note: hole diameter = 915 mm

6.3.5   Geophysics

Downhole geophysics should be able to make important contributions to an appreciation of the local stratigraphy in the Lambeth Group, particularly if correlations are established at the outset using continuous rotary cores. It should be possible to identify sand bodies and to provide key information on levels of cementing, via the latter's influence on body wave velocities.

Geophysical logging, using calliper, sonic, natural gamma and gamma backscatter sondes, was carried out successfully in cased and mud-filled boreholes at various sites on JLE. Typical profiles are presented in Figure 6.3, together with a summary of the geology inferred from the profiles. It is evident that the units, and sub-divisions within the units, are distinguishable on the basis of the sonic velocity, natural gamma and gamma backscatter logs. See Figure 2.8 for an example of a gamma log taken from a borehole in central London.

Ground-penetrating radar may prove useful in locating solution holes.

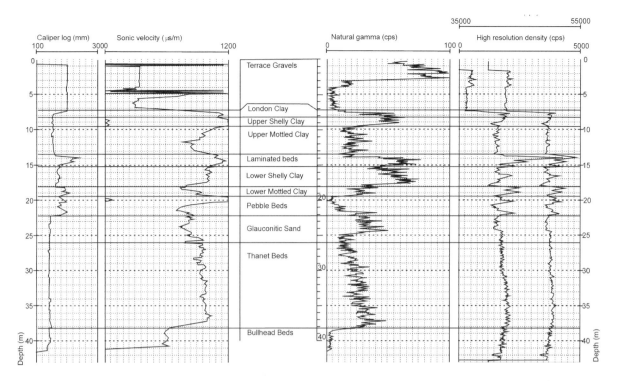

Figure 6.3 *Results of down-hole logging, Bermondsey, JLE*

6.4 SAMPLING METHODS

Sampling methods used in ground investigations in the Lambeth Group are described below.

6.4.1 Block sampling

Block sampling of the clay units within the Lambeth Group below London has been carried out from the base of shafts and from the face and side-walls of tunnels during their construction. The potential damage to clays in the face of tunnels is discussed in Section 6.6.

6.4.2 Driven thick-wall tube sampling

The conventional U100 sampling tube is widely used to obtain samples for both inspection and laboratory testing. While adequate for basic lithological identification and index testing, samples, particularly those of cemented clays and sands, are likely to be seriously disturbed and laboratory strength and stiffness measurements made on them are unlikely to be representative of *in-situ* values (see Section 6.6).

6.4.3 Pushed thin-wall tube sampling

Thin-wall Shelby tubes (102 mm diameter, 2 mm wall thickness and 1 m or 0.6 m long) have been successfully pushed into the clay units of the Lambeth Group on JLE. However, buckling of the tube or crimping of the cutting edge occurs and there appears to be an upper limit to undrained shear strength of 200–250 kN/m², above which the technique will not work. Obviously, pushed thin-wall tubes cannot penetrate hard layers without damage to themselves and any further soil that they capture.

6.4.4 Rotary coring

Double-tube core barrel

While any rotary technique has the advantage of permitting continuous sampling, so necessary for establishing stratigraphy, difficulties arise with a double-tube core barrel, because of:

- disturbance to the sample in the inner barrel during drilling
- softening of the sample by drilling fluids trapped in the inner barrel
- damage to the sample when removing it from the inner barrel.

Triple-tube core barrel

Some of the drawbacks to a double-tube core barrel are eliminated in a triple-tube core barrel, in which a semi-rigid plastic lining tube is inserted within the inner core barrel. The liner supports the sample during drilling and during removal from the core barrel and subsequent handling (Scarrow and Gosling, 1986).

Triple-tube core barrels with biodegradable mud flush were used successfully in investigations for Limehouse Link, JLE, CTRL, DLR.

Wireline drilling with triple-tube core barrel

Wireline drilling involves the use of a large-diameter drill string, which remains in the borehole and through which the core barrel is lowered and retrieved on a wire. The advantages of wireline coring over conventional coring include the following:

- the drill string cases the borehole as drilling progresses, preventing caving and the collection of debris at the base of the borehole
- separate temporary casing for borehole stabilisation is not required
- withdrawal of the core barrel inside the casing avoids damage to the walls of the borehole, which would otherwise occur
- the thin (3 mm) annulus between the drill string and borehole wall requires significantly lower volumes of flush fluid and lower flush velocities in comparison with conventional drilling, and this reduces core and borehole wall erosion
- the drill string is more rigid, reducing the risk of core damage due to rocking of the core barrel
- the time taken to withdraw the core barrel is greatly reduced, which means that damage due to swelling of the core can also be reduced, provided that the core is immediately removed from the barrel, cleaned and sealed.

Wireline drilling with triple-tube core barrels has been used in the Lambeth Group at Waterloo International Terminal (Hight *et al*, 1993; Pickles and Everton, 1996), for the JLE (Linney and Page, 1996) and for CTRL (Beckwith *et al*, 1996).

Drill bits

Drilling-induced core disturbance can be reduced by the use of face discharge drill bits, and tungsten or diamond impregnated bits can cope with the hard strata in the Lambeth Group.

Recommendations for drilling bits to be used in the Lambeth Group are given by Beckwith *et al* (1996), based on their experience in the CTRL investigations. For both the Woolwich and Reading Formations, they suggest diamond saw-tooth bits. When problems of core loss occurred, because of erosion of the matrix, these were resolved by switching to tungsten carbide bits and changing from a biodegradable polymer mud flush. In the Upnor Formation, the ideal bit configuration was found to be diamond-set. Drill bits used at Sizewell are reported by Hepton (1996) to have been face discharge, seven-step, surface-set, diamond bits, set to cut a 146 mm hole and 102 mm-diameter core.

A disadvantage of wireline drilling is that the drill bit cannot be examined or changed without withdrawing the complete drill string. It is obviously preferable to use a single all-purpose bit and to ensure that poor recoveries are not the result of persistent use of a worn drill bit.

Polymer flushes have been used successfully during rotary coring in the Lambeth Group.

Core loss

Core losses occur, even with the most careful drilling, particularly in the sands and gravels of the Upnor and Woolwich Formations. Examples of the extent of core losses can be seen in the core photographs presented in Appendix 2. Where core losses occur, information can be obtained from down-hole geophysics.

Preservation of samples

Techniques for minimising the swelling of rotary cored samples have been introduced and involve:

- the immediate removal of the core from its plastic liner, by cutting the liner on diametrically opposite sides without scoring the core
- removing drilling fluid from the surface of the core and trimming away the outer skin of softened material
- sealing the core in alternate layers of low-temperature wax and clingfilm
- protecting the sealed core in plastic pipe and placing in a core box to prevent damage during transit.

6.5 SAMPLING EFFECTS

The effects of sampling in some of the units of the Lambeth Group appear to be especially severe. This is associated with their particular fabric, layering, hardness, presence of pebbles, and with the methods conventionally used to obtain samples. Some of these effects are referred to in preceding sections.

6.5.1 Effects of laminations

Several of the units are laminated or interbedded (see Section 4.4) and the laminated fabric persists to a fine scale, down to a millimetre. When a sample is taken from the ground and relieved of its *in-situ* boundary stresses, negative pore water pressures, or suctions, are set up within the sample. The more permeable laminae or beds within the sample may not be able to sustain the imposed suction, which will depend, *inter alia*, on the depth from which the sample was taken. The pore water in the more permeable zones will be free to be drawn into the less permeable zones, where suctions have been sustained. Inevitably, there will be water content redistribution within the sample: uncemented clay layers will swell and increase in water content and silt and sand layers will reduce in water content – air will invade the latter.

The presence of more permeable layers will also accelerate the process of swelling and the take-up of water from flushing media or from seepage into the borehole, during rotary coring or boring – this is discussed in the next sub-section.

Water content measurements in laminated units will not, therefore, be representative of *in-situ* water contents. This can be demonstrated most easily by re-examining data for liquidity index, in which the effects of varying plasticity are effectively normalised out. The stress history of the units and their depth of burial (see Section 4.3) are such that I_L could be expected to be zero or less. Values above zero might be expected where the units are near ground surface and have swelled naturally. Variations of I_L with depth for JLE, Crossrail and CTRL are presented in Figures 4.27 and 4.28. As noted in Section 4.9, there is a large scatter in all the plots, with I_L values significantly above and below zero.

This scatter and the occurrence of I_L values, both well above and well below zero, would be consistent with the water content redistribution in laminated/bedded material described above. The effect of water content redistribution and the scatter is likely to be more noticeable in soils of lower plasticity for the following reasons.

1   Inevitable mixing of clay and sand (or silt) laminae in preparing samples for Atterberg Limit tests means that laminated units will tend to be associated with lower plasticity index.

2   By definition of I_L, a given change in water content has more influence as I_p reduces.

This is borne out by the plot in Figure 6.4, which shows the variation in I_L with I_p, using data from the CTRL Tunnels and Stratford Box. The spread in I_L values, involving both high and low values is much greater at low I_p; more consistent I_L values are associated with soils of high plasticity.

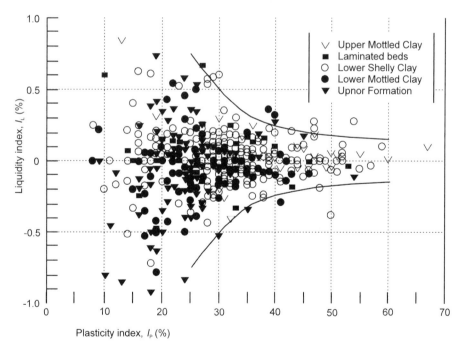

Figure 6.4   *Comparison of I_L and I_p for Stratford Box, London Tunnels West and London Tunnels East*

6.5.2   Effects of swelling

During rotary coring, the sample is exposed to drilling fluids from which it can absorb water, causing the suction to reduce and allowing the sample to swell. There is much evidence to show that suctions remaining in rotary cores are considerably lower than suctions remaining in tube samples. An example from an investigation in the Lambeth Group is shown in Figure 6.5. In the different units the initial effective stress, ρ_i, in the rotary cored samples are less than half of the values in thin-wall tube samples taken from similar depths.

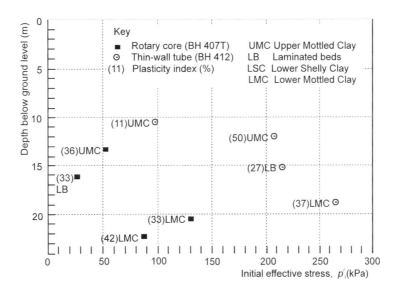

Figure 6.5 *Comparison of initial effective stresses in rotary cored and thin-wall tube samples*

The laminations in the different units of the Lambeth Group, discussed above, mean that the swelling process during rotary coring is relatively rapid. Reductions in suction tend to be larger than those that occur in the London Clay. A comparison of suctions measured in rotary cores of London Clay and the Lambeth Group is presented in Figure 6.6 to illustrate this point and the scatter in suction values that is found in rotary cores from the Lambeth Group.

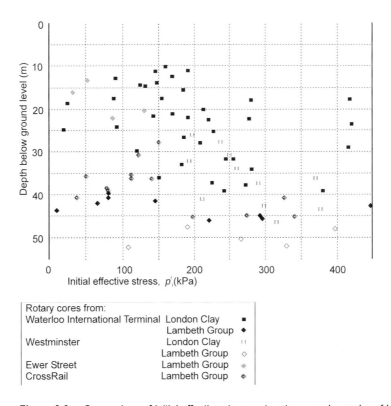

Figure 6.6 *Comparison of initial effective stresses in rotary cored samples of London Clay and Lambeth Group*

The loss of suction in more permeable zones will result in their losing coherence and apparent stiffness and strength, unless they are cemented and this has been retained. Swelling of clay layers, irrespective of whether they are in laminated units, may have a damaging effect on cementation, depending on the strength of the cement and the swelling forces that develop, which are likely to increase with soil plasticity.

The effects of swelling appear to be particularly severe in the fissured mottled clays in which it is thought that the fissures were cemented during pedogenesis (see Section 4.3). Figure 4.48 shows effective stress paths from rotary cored samples of Upper Mottled Clay and Lower Mottled Clay, taken as part of the Crossrail investigation. The effective stress paths for samples of high plasticity ($I_p > 30\%$), which are known to have swelled to low effective stresses ($p'_i < 150$ kPa) prior to UU or CIU triaxial compression, define a lower bound failure line, corresponding to $c' = 0$, $\varphi' = 14.5°$. Failure would appear to be governed by the strength on fissures, which are known to be closely spaced and polished because of seasonal movements (see Section 4.3) – hence the low value for φ' of 14.5°. The effects of any cementing across fissures appears to have been lost. Effective stress paths for samples that did not swell initially to such low values of mean effective stress define a much higher failure envelope, with a substantial cohesion intercept.

The evidence in Figure 4.48 from Sample 8, which is of a similar low plasticity to Sample 5, but which swelled to much lower effective stress ($p'_i = 112$ kPa, *cf* 422 kPa) indicates that swelling can also cause damage in the lower-plasticity clays, if swelling to low effective stresses occurs. However, damage due to swelling appears to be much more likely in the higher-plasticity clays.

A second example of damage resulting from swelling of rotary cored samples is provided by data from Sizewell. The results of a series of CIU triaxial compression tests on 100 mm-diameter specimens cut from rotary cored samples of Upper Mottled Clay, taken from depths between 62 m and 72 m at Sizewell, are shown in Figure 6.7. The peak effective stress states are shown in relation to the peak and post-rupture failure envelopes established for the Upper Mottled Clay at WIT and Crossrail. Also shown are the initial stress states after isotropic consolidation, which can be used with the failure points to give an indication of the average slope of the effective stress path.

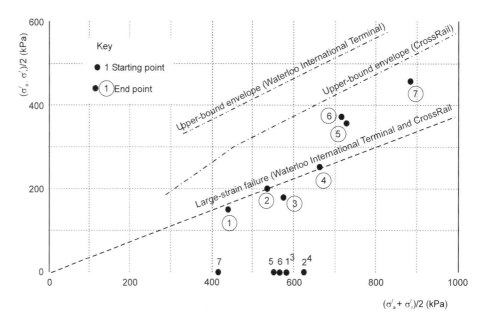

Figure 6.7   *Effects of swelling in rotary cored samples, Sizewell C*

The average slope of the effective stress paths for four of the samples (4, 5, 6 and 7) is typical of that for the Upper Mottled Clay observed at WIT. Of these, the peak points for 5, 6 and 7 lie reasonably close to the upper bound envelope for Crossrail. Sample 4 lies on the post-rupture failure envelope, suggesting that failure occurred on a natural or induced discontinuity. For samples 1, 2 and 3, the stress path slopes are atypical and the peak points lie on or below the post-rupture failure envelope. It is probable that these rotary cored samples had been damaged by swelling. The differences in strength apparent in these CIU tests is not reflected in the SPT or CPT data (see Figure 4.74).

6.5.3   Effects of tube sampling strains in clays

The strains caused by pushing or driving a sampling tube into clay can cause damage to the structure, including any cementing that may be present. The fissured and cemented clays of the Reading Formation would appear to be particularly prone to sampling disturbance because the tube sampling strains are likely to cause movement on existing fissures, damaging the cementing across them and allowing them to take on a dominant, yet unrepresentative role in the subsequent behaviour of the clays.

In hard brittle clays, the energy released at the tip of a driven thick-wall sampling tube causes fractures to propagate from the tip. The sample is sometimes shattered as a result, and its density is reduced. Experience suggests that this happens when the undrained strength in these materials exceeds 200–250 kPa, which is the case for deeply buried clay units of the Lambeth Group.

The results of a series of UU and CIU triaxial compression tests on driven thick-wall tube (U100) samples of Upper and Lower Mottled Clays are shown in Figure 4.49. Two failure envelopes are shown, which approximately bound the data: one corresponding to $c' = 0$ and $\varphi' = 24°$ and one corresponding to $c' = 0$ and $\varphi' = 12°$. With one exception, Sample 3, the data is for samples having plasticity indices greater than 30 per cent. Although initial effective stresses were not measured in these samples, it is unlikely that the samples swelled to the low effective stresses reached by the rotary cored samples. Damage due to swelling can probably be ruled out. Instead, there is likely to have been movement on fissures in preferred directions, controlled by the pattern of straining imposed by driving in the sampling tube. Movement causing damage to cementing on critically oriented fissures accounts for failures occurring at $c' = 0$, $\varphi' = 12°$. Movement on fissures in other preferred directions will have reduced the overall strength, but with some fissures unaffected and retaining their cementation, this strength is greater than that measured on the core samples, which swelled to low effective stresses, and in which the damage to fissures was omnidirectional. It is probably significant that the peak failure envelope in Figure 4.49 for these samples damaged by tube sampling strains ($c' = 0$ and $\varphi' = 24°$), corresponds to the large strain or post-rupture failure envelope defined in Figure 4.47 for initially undamaged samples.

Damage due to tube sampling strains not only affects strengths, but also expansibility. Table 6.2 compares the coefficients of expansibility, m_s, measured in oedometer swelling tests on both rotary cored and thin-wall tube samples of different units from the Lambeth Group. m_s is consistently higher, by more than a factor of two in the case of the Upper Mottled Clay, in the tube samples than in the rotary cores. This is the result of damage to cementing in the tube samples.

Table 6.2 *Comparison of expansibility measured in rotary cored and thin-wall tube samples*

Unit	UMC Depth (m)	UMC m_s (m²/MN)	Lb Depth (m)	Lb m_s (m²/MN)	LMC Depth (m)	LMC M (m²/MN)	LSC Depth (m)	LSC m_s (m²/MN)
Rotary core	13.34	0.114	16.13	0.146	22.15	0.157	20.35	0.056
Thin-wall tube	11.9	0.314	15.1	0.205	18.7	0.304	–	

m_s measured in swelling up to 10 kPa

Other possible effects of tube sampling strains concern the following.

1 *Their impact on measured bulk densities.* Hight and Jardine (1993) have shown that, in hard plastic clays, driven tube samples underestimate bulk density, because of the fractures that propagate into the samples. Low values of bulk density, below 1.95 Mg/m³, are usually associated with tube samples, see Figure 6.8 for an example.

2 *Their influence on water content redistribution.* Tube sampling strains damage cementing, so that swelling after sampling is less restricted; water content redistribution may be more noticeable, therefore, in damaged samples than in rotary cored samples. High values of I_L are often associated with driven tube samples, see Figure 6.9 for an example.

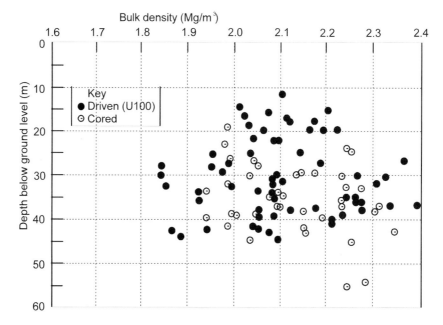

Figure 6.8 *Comparison of bulk densities measured on driven and cored samples, Crossrail*

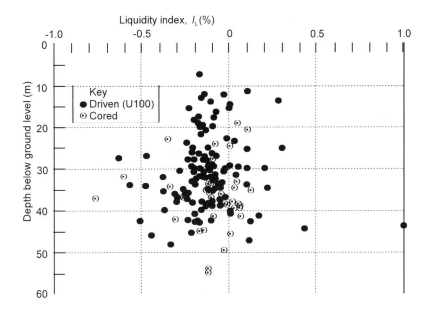

Figure 6.9 *Liquidity index from driven and cored samples*

6.5.4 Effects of tube sampling in sands

The effects of tube sampling in sands depend on their initial density. The dense sand units of the Lambeth Group are likely to reduce in density as a result of tube sampling strains.

6.5.5 Damage to block samples

In addition to the block sample of Upper Mottled Clay taken from the tunnel face at Angel Station, both pushed thin-wall and driven thick-wall tube samples were taken as part of the pre-design site investigation. The results of undrained triaxial compression tests on 100 mm-diameter specimens cut from the tube samples are shown in Figure 6.10, together with the data from a 38 mm-diameter specimen cut from a block sample. Also shown are the peak- and post-rupture failure envelopes found for the Upper Mottled Clay at WIT. None of the specimens exhibit the undrained brittleness seen in the rotary cored samples from WIT. In fact, as with the driven tube samples at Crossrail, a more relevant failure envelope appears to be the post-rupture envelope defined at WIT, although the specimen from the thick-wall tube sample falls some way below this.

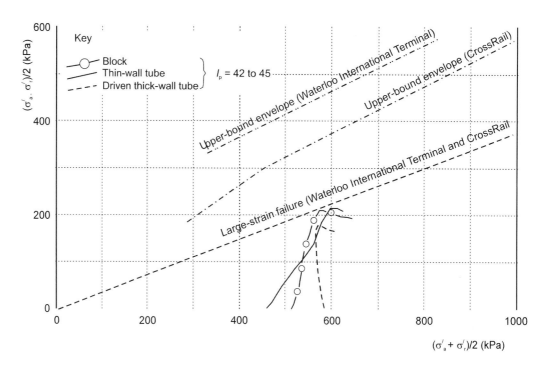

Figure 6.10 *Evidence of damage to block samples taken from tunnel side-wall, Angel Station, Islington*

The results are, therefore, consistent with important disturbance having occurred. Disturbance to the block samples could be related to their being taken from the tunnel face, where yielding of the clay could be expected (Mair and Taylor, 1993) if

$$\frac{\sigma_{v0}}{c_u} > \frac{4}{3}$$

Taking c_u as 400 kPa, then at a depth of 34 m and with $\gamma = 20$ kN/m³

$$\frac{\sigma_{v0}}{c_u} = \frac{680}{400} = 1.7 > \frac{4}{3}$$

Evidence for yielding of the soil prior to being taken as blocks is provided by the very high initial effective stresses in triaxial specimens trimmed from the block. Values in excess of 800 kPa were recorded and these exceed the estimated *in-situ* mean effective stress p'_0, by more than 60 per cent. In heavily overconsolidated clays, shearing to failure followed by unloading can cause increases in p' of this order. Shearing in the tunnel face is likely to have led to damage on inclined surfaces rather than on horizontal surfaces. Such surfaces will downgrade triaxial shear strength but not strengths in direct shear, where failure is constrained to take place on horizontal surfaces. As described in Section 4.13, high strengths and brittle behaviour were observed in direct shear tests on specimens cut from the same block samples.

Damage to the tube samples is feasible because of the tube sampling strains imposed, as discussed above. These strains will be larger for the driven thick-wall tube and it is, perhaps, significant that the specimen from this tube has the lowest strength.

6.5.6   Summary

Rotary coring causes:

- damage to cementing as a result of swelling in the presence of the drilling fluid
- reductions in effective stress.

Higher-plasticity clays seem to be much more liable to be damaged by swelling, particularly if there has been damage to cementing prior to swelling. Swelling to mean effective stresses of less than 200–300 kPa seems to cause damage in deep samples of low-plasticity clays below central London.

Tube sampling, especially driven thick-wall tube sampling, causes:

- damage to cementing, particularly when it leads to movement on cemented fissures
- the propagation of fractures from the tube's cutting edge when driven into hard brittle clays; these reduce density
- changes in effective stress.

The different patterns of behaviour in uncemented low- and high-plasticity clays, described in Section 4.1.3, mean that their response to sampling, and the effects of sampling, also differ for the different types of clay. Therefore, in terms of undrained strength, sampled clays of low plasticity are sensitive to changes in water content as a result of sampling, and less so to changes in effective stress, whereas sampled clays of high plasticity are sensitive to changes in initial effective stress.

Strengths measured in UU triaxial compression tests on U100 samples of high-plasticity clays from the Lambeth Group, may be seriously underestimated. High strengths may be measured in rotary cored samples if these have been prevented from swelling.

6.6 LABORATORY TESTING

6.6.1 Index properties

Although of limited value in distinguishing between units, establishing the Atterberg Limits is vital in interpreting the strength and stiffness of the soils. Plasticity indices span the range of 25–30 per cent, which usually provides a boundary between:

- clays that bifurcate ($I_p > 25$–30%) and clays that can dilate without bifurcation ($I_p < 25$–30%)
- fissures, shear surface, joints that may be polished ($I_p > 25$–30%)
- clays with a large potential to swell and damage cementing ($I_p > 25$–30%).

In the laminated or interbedded soils care should be taken to avoid mixing of layers in order to obtain representative measurements.

6.6.2 Bulk unit weight

There often appears to be a correlation between strength and unit weight in the clays, the highest strengths being measured in the densest samples. Reliable measurements of unit weight, recalling the potential effects on them of driven tube sampling are important, therefore, and essential for the interpretation of body wave measurements.

6.6.3 Geochemistry

The petrology of the samples should be determined and checks made for the presence of potentially deleterious minerals such as pyrite and gypsum, particularly if the sediments are likely to be exposed to free air where problems of agressivity, durability and oxygen depletion from confined atmospheres are suspected. Cation exchange capacity and mineralogy should be determined if risk from swelling clays exists.

6.6.4 Evaluation of sample quality

Sample quality may be assessed on the basis of comparisons between.

1   The initial effective stress in the sample, p_i' and the value of mean effective stress *in situ*, at the depth from which the sample was taken, p_o'.

2   The shear wave velocities in the sample after it has been reconsolidated to *in-situ* stresses and those measured at the same depth *in situ*, using cross-hole and down-hole techniques.

Alternatively, an assessment may be made on the basis of the change in void ratio, Δe, during reconsolidation to *in-situ* stresses, expressed as $\Delta e/e_o$, where e_o is the initial void ratio.

6.6.5 Strength and stiffness measurements

As noted above, sampling can result in a change in effective stress, water content and density, as well as damage to cementing. Initial effective stresses, p_i', are variable, especially in rotary cored samples (see Figure 6.6). Damage in driven U100 samples is inconsistent.

In unconsolidated undrained (UU) triaxial compression tests, there is no control over p_i'. Sampling effects add to the variability in the natural material, when strengths are measured in UU tests on U100 or rotary cored samples.

Strength testing should involve high-quality samples with the measurement of pore pressures and interpretation in terms of effective stress. On high-plasticity clay samples initial effective stresses should preferably be controlled, by running isotropically consolidated (CI) or anisotropically consolidated (CA) tests, with the samples reconsolidated to estimated *in-situ* effective stresses. On low-plasticity clay samples, changes in water content should be avoided. Tests should be continued to large strains to measure ultimate post-rupture strengths.

For reliable measurements of non-linear stiffness characteristics on both high- and low-plasticity clays, reconsolidation paths should trace the *in-situ* soil's recent stress history with proper allowance for creep, and both axial and radial displacements in triaxial tests should be measured using instrumentation mounted on the sample over a central gauge length.

6.7 BEST PRACTICE FOR GROUND INVESTIGATIONS IN THE LAMBETH GROUP

6.7.1 Conventional practice

Until relatively recently, conventional site investigation practice in the Lambeth Group has involved standard penetration testing and sampling by driven thick-wall tubes, with measurements of stiffness and strength in unconsolidated undrained (UU) triaxial compression tests, usually without the measurement of pore water pressures and relying on external measurements of axial displacement.

Discontinuous sampling and the difficulties of obtaining full length samples meant that key layers, such as hard bands or water-bearing sands, may have been missed. Insufficient sampling and lack of understanding of the stratigraphy have led to the mis-assigning of units and confusion over the engineering properties of the Group.

The effects of damage by tube sampling strains and the errors involved in measuring axial displacements externally have meant that both strength and stiffness have almost certainly been seriously underestimated.

6.7.2   Best practice

The aim would be to establish the local stratigraphy in a site-specific investigation, to establish the scale of natural variability in relevant properties and to identify the potential engineering hazards.

Best practice for ground investigation for a major project in the Lambeth Group would select from the following.

1   Rotary coring to obtain continuous cores for detailed examination of stratigraphy and fabric and for provision of samples, suitably preserved, for index testing. Both descriptive and interpretative logs should be produced (by an experienced geologist) and a photographic record of the cores, to the quality shown in Appendix 2, should be provided. The description of fabric should include a detailed record of fissure spacing, orientation and surface texture, and of laminae spacing, thickness and composition.

2   Rotary coring to obtain high-quality samples for laboratory testing to measure stiffness, strength and permeability. It is essential that swelling and other disturbances of these samples are minimised. Target depths for sampling should be selected on the basis of (1).

3   Down-hole geophysics to provide continuous profiles with the following sondes:
    ● calliper – to obtain borehole geometry
    ● sonic – to record P wave velocities over different fixed lengths
    ● natural gamma – to identify changes in material type
    ● gamma-gamma – to obtain a density profile
    ● electrical resistivity.

4   Cross-hole and down-hole seismic body wave measurements in suitably cased boreholes.

5   *In-situ* testing as appropriate:
    ● SPT
    ● CPTU
    ● plate testing
    ● permeability
    ● pressuremeter.

6   Laboratory strength testing involving the measurement of pore pressure in undrained tests and interpretation in terms of effective stresses.

7   Laboratory stiffness measurements involving the use of local instrumentation and appropriate reconsolidation paths.

6.8   ASSESSING ENGINEERING PROPERTIES AND SELECTING DESIGN PARAMETERS

6.8.1   Natural and induced variability

The key characteristic of the Lambeth Group is its variability in terms of stratigraphy, lithology and engineering properties. The group comprises interbedded layers of very stiff to hard fissured silty clays, dense to very dense sands, gravels and duricrusts. Individual units may be absent at some locations. There are rapid and abrupt changes in lithology. Hard layers, in the form of duricrusts and limestones, are impersistent.

In assessing engineering properties, natural variability needs to be distinguished from induced variability, ie variability introduced by the effects of different levels of disturbance during sampling and preparation for laboratory testing, and by shortcomings in the test itself.

The natural variability in engineering properties is related to the variable composition, environments of deposition, and post-depositional processes that have occurred. These sources of natural variability in engineering properties are summarised in Table 6.3. They are discussed in more detail below, together with the particular sources of induced variability.

Table 6.3   *Sources of natural variability in engineering properties*

Source of natural variability
I_p straddling 25 per cent
– $I_p < 25\%$ $\varphi'_r \approx \varphi'_p$ / dilatant/non-fissured or fissures not of low strength
– $I_p > 30\%$ $\varphi'_r \ll \varphi'_p$ / bifurcates/fissured at various scales
Laminated fabric at various scales
Variable cementing
Fissures of varying strength, possibly cemented, and of variable spacing and orientation
Swelling – variable I_p and resistance to swelling forces
Desiccation – duricrusts
Recent weathering

6.8.2   Composition

Plasticity indices vary within each clay unit and between units, straddling the value of 25 per cent (see Figures 4.12 and 4.13). Stiff clays having the mineralogy of the Lambeth Group (see Section 4.8) show two distinct patterns of behaviour, depending whether they are of low plasticity, I_p less than approximately 25 per cent, or of high plasticity, I_p more than 35 per cent. Low-plasticity clays are non-brittle and have a residual angle of shearing resistance, φ'_r, close to that at peak, φ'_p (see Figure 4.40). They are able to dilate during shear without bifurcation, large strengths can be mobilised in undrained shear (Figure 4.41) and the response is ductile. Undrained strength is a function of water content.

More plastic clays show a significant drop in friction angle from peak to residual and brittle behaviour. The clays tend to bifurcate during shear so that undrained strength is a function of initial effective stress (Figure 4.41). Major differences in undrained strength can be expected, then, between clays of low and high plasticity. In the absence of other factors, such as fissuring and cementing, discussed below, clays having similar stress histories but of low plasticity can be expected to exhibit higher undrained strengths than clays of high plasticity (see for example Figures 4.43 to 4.45).

Superimposed on this natural difference/variability due to composition are the effects of sampling. The undrained strength in low-plasticity clays will be modified by changes in water content. Small changes in water content can cause a large change in undrained strength, increasing the range in measured strengths. The strengths measured in UU tests on high-plasticity clays will be modified by changes in initial effective stress, which themselves will vary. The spread of data will increase and overestimates of strength are possible in uncemented clays.

6.8.3   Initial fabric

Several of the units in the Lambeth Group are laminated at different scales. For example the Laminated beds have individual beds that are less than 50 mm thick and are finely laminated down to 1 mm. Permeability, strength and stiffness vary between layers, introducing important anisotropy.

Again superimposed on this natural variability are the particular effects of sampling associated with this initial fabric. Thus laminae at a fine scale may result in measurements of Atterberg Limits being unrepresentative. Different permeabilities and levels of sustainable suction may result in water content redistribution between layers on stress relief.

6.8.4   Cementing

Cementing in the Upper and Lower Mottled and Shelly Clays is variable. For example, where shell layers are concentrated limestone bands have developed; elsewhere carbonate cementing is likely to decrease within increasing distance from shell layers. This contributes to the natural variability in the strength of these clays, both at a particular site and between sites. Swelling as a result of unloading, and the swelling forces to be resisted by cementing before damage, will be greater the more plastic the clay. Thus the effects of cementing are more likely to be retained in the low-plasticity clays after unloading.

Additional variability and the likelihood of underestimates of strength result from disturbance, which damages cementing by different amounts. This may occur as a result of the following.

1   Shear strains imposed by pushing in a thin-wall tube, or by driving in a thick-wall tube, or by excavation to gain access to a sample, for example from the face of a deep tunnel.

2   Volumetric strains caused by swelling of rotary cored specimens or redistribution of water content in laminated or layered samples. Swelling is more likely if some damage to cementing has already occurred, for example by any strains inadvertently applied during rotary coring.

The effects of cementing may overwrite to some extent the effects of differences in plasticity within each unit, which have been described above. Where cementing has not occurred, or has been damaged, the effects of differences in plasticity will be felt.

6.8.5   Fissuring

The effects of fissures depends on both the plasticity of the clay and whether or not the fissures are cemented and the cementing has remained intact. Polished low-strength fissures appear to be restricted to the higher-plasticity clays. Where uncemented, or where the cementing has been damaged, these fissures will have a major effect on both undrained and drained strength. Unfavourably oriented fissures give rise to a failure envelope corresponding to $c' = 0$, $\varphi' = 14.5°$. Cementing can overwrite the effect of polished fissures, but appears to be easily damaged by shear and volumetric strains.

Fissures in low-plasticity clays, if present, are less likely to be polished, unless they have been infilled by plastic clay. High strengths have been measured in fissured low-plasticity clays suggesting that either the fissures were not represented, or they have little impact on strength, or they were cemented. The last is believed to be the case.

Fissures introduce natural variability through differences in fissure spacing, orientation and form. Superimposed on this natural variability are again the effects of sampling and testing, particularly specimen size. Higher-plasticity clays of the Upper and Lower Mottled Clay are usually described as extremely or very closely fissured – 100 mm-diameter specimens should be representative, therefore, in terms of fissuring. Fissures tend to be more widely spaced in low-plasticity clays and may not necessarily be represented in test specimens. Movement on fissures during sampling can modify both stiffness and strength.

6.8.6   Selection of design parameters

As a result of its restricted outcrop and limited depth there are few data available on the performance of structures, the behaviour of which has been controlled by the Lambeth Group alone. Correlations between *in-situ* tests and performance or engineering properties developed for other materials may not be appropriate and will in any event be difficult to apply. For example the use of SPT – undrained strength correlations that depend on soil plasticity have to contend both with the typical scatter in the SPT N values (Figures 4.68 to 4.70) and the variability in plasticity (Figures 4.17 to 4.19).

Dealing with natural variability, once this has been isolated, depends on the scale of variability and whether performance will be governed by a weak layer or by an integrated response. Bounds need to be set to the level of variability. An integrated response, where relevant, needs to be established on the basis of *in-situ* measurements, for example using large-diameter plate tests, or by analysis that takes into account strain compatibility. Strain compatibility is relevant to assessing operational strength where clays of high and low plasticity co-exist, with their very different character. Anisotropy resulting from layering, as well as within layers, needs to be taken into account.

In the selection of undrained strength and stiffness, it needs to be recognised that conventional measurements, using UU tests on U100 samples, can lead to gross underestimates in the brittle cemented plastic clays. Similar underestimates can occur in samples that are allowed to swell, for example as a result of rotary coring. Equally, major reductions in strength can occur naturally as a result of swelling during and after construction.

The natural variability and the difficulties in establishing its level, together with uncertainty over *in-situ* stresses and rates of pore pressure dissipation during construction in these interbedded deposits, means that observational methods are entirely appropriate within the Lambeth Group, with initial designs based on carefully selected bounds.

7   Further work

7.1   CHARACTERISATION STUDIES

Understanding of the engineering behaviour of the units that make up the Lambeth Group is incomplete. The picture so far has been built up on the basis of inadequate data, from tests on samples that may have been damaged to varying extents. State-of-the-art ground investigations should be carried out at a minimum of two sites in the London Basin, one typical of the Lambeth Group at depth, and one typical of the Lambeth Group at surface. The investigations should comprise the following.

1   Appropriate *in-situ* testing

- geophysics, including down-hole and cross-hole seismic surveys
- plate testing in boreholes or in trial pits, depending on feasibility
- CPTU testing
- permeability testing.

2   Continuous rotary coring to provide a complete sequence for detailed logging, photography, fabric description (including scanning electron microscopy) and index testing.

3   Selective rotary coring to provide high-quality undisturbed samples, carefully preserved, for laboratory testing.

4   Laboratory testing to include measurements of:

- strength, in terms of effective stresses
- non-linear stiffness characteristics, both shear and volumetric
- swelling properties, including the process of destructuring by swelling and the progressive reduction in strength.

There is a requirement, both for the engineering properties of individual units within the Lambeth Group and for guidance on how these properties may be integrated, to estimate the response of several units in combination. This guidance could come through numerical parametric studies.

Performance data for structures built on or within the Lambeth Group is sparse and links between performance data, as well as engineering properties, and simply measured index properties have not been firmly established. More work is required to develop these links.

7.2   CASE HISTORIES

Fully documented case histories of construction in the Lambeth Group are essential to improving understanding of its behaviour and predictions of performance of structures. It is essential that this information (for both small and large projects in the London and Hampshire Basins) is widely disseminated.

References

ANDREWS, R D (1990)
Determining the age of failure of motorway embankments from aerial photographs
Research Report RR257, Transport Research Laboratory, Crowthorne

BAKER, A C J and JAMES, A N (1990)
Three Valleys Water Committee: tunnel connection to Thames Water Reservoirs
Proc Inst Civ Engrs, vol 88, no 1, pp 929–954

BARROW, G (1905)
Some future work for the Geologists' Association
Proc Geologists' Association, vol 30, pp 1–20

BATEMAN, R M and MOFFAT, A J (1987)
Petrography of the Woolwich and Reading Formation (Late Palaeocene) of the Chiltern
Hill, Southern Hills
Southern England Tertiary research, vol 8, pp 75–103

BATTEN, M, POWRIE, W, BOORMAN, R and YU, H (1996)
Measurement of prop loads in large braced excavation during construction of the JLE
station at Canada Water, East London
*Proc int symp geotechnical aspects of underground construction in soft ground, City
University, London*, AA Balkema, Rotterdam

BECKWITH, R C, RANKIN, W J, BLIGHT, I C and HARRISON, I (1996)
Overview of initial ground investigations for the Channel Tunnel high speed rail link
In: *Proc int conf advances in site investigation practice*, Thomas Telford, London,
pp 119–144

BLONDEAU, A and POMEROL, C (1968)
A contribution to the sedimentological study of the Palaeogene of England
In: *Proc Geological Association*, vol 79, pp 441–455

BLYTH, R S (1994)
The Limehouse Link
Proc Inst Civ Engrs, Civ engg, vol 102, May, Paper 10483, pp 56–63

BRACEGIRDLE, A, JEFFERIS, S A, TEDD, P, CRAMMOND, N J, CHUDLEIGH, I
and BURGESS, N (1996a)
The investigation of acid generation within the Woolwich and Reading Beds at Old
Street and its effects on tunnel linings
In: *Proc int symp geotechnical aspects of underground construction in soft ground, City
University, London*, AA Balkema, Rotterdam

BRACEGIRDLE, A, MAIR, R J, NYREN R J and TAYLOR, R N (1996b)
A simple methodology for evaluating the potential damage to buried cast iron pipes
from ground movements
In: *Proc int symp geotechnical aspects of underground construction in soft ground, City
University, London*, AA Balkema, Rotterdam

BRISTOW, C R (1985)
Geology of the country around Chelmsford
Memoir of the British Geological Survey, Sheet E241

BRISTOW, C R, FRESHNEY, E C and PENN, I E (1991)
Geology of the country around Bournemouth
Memoir of the British Geological Survey, Sheet E329

BROMEHEAD, C E N (1922)
Excursion to Brockley, Bromley Park and Beckenham, Saturday June 16th, 1921
Proc Geologists' Association, vol 33, Part 1, pp 77–78

BROMHEAD, E N (1979)
Factors affecting the transition between the various types of mass movement in coastal
cliffs consisting largely of overconsolidated clay with special reference to Southern
England
Q J engineering geology, vol 12, pp 291–300

BURLAND, J B (1969)
Contribution to discussion
In: *Proc conf on in-situ investigations in soils and rocks,* Brit Geotech Soc, London

BURLAND, J B (1973)
Shaft friction of piles in clay – a simple fundamental approach
Ground engineering, vol 6, no 3, pp 30–42

BURLAND, J B, MAIR, R J, LINNEY, L F, JARDINE, F M and STANDING, J R (1996)
A collaborative research programme on subsidence damage to buildings: prediction,
protection and repair
In: *Proc int symp geotechnical aspects of underground construction in soft ground, City
University, London*, AA Balkema, Rotterdam

BUURMAN, P (1980)
Palaeosols in the Reading Beds (Palaeocene) of Alum Bay, Isle of Wight, UK
Sedimentology, vol 27, pp 593–606

CARON, C, DELISLE, J P and GODDEN, W H (1963)
Resin grouting, with special reference to the treatment of the silty fine sand of the
Woolwich and Reading Beds at the New Blackwall Tunnel
In: *Proc symp grouts and drilling muds in engineering practice*, Butterworths, London

CHANDLER, R J (1984)
Recent European experience of landslides in overconsolidated clays and soft rocks
In: *Proc 4th int symp landslides, Toronto*, vol 1, Univ Toronto, Toronto, pp 61–81

CHANDLER, R J, CRILLY, M S and MONTGOMERY-SMITH, G (1992)
A low cost method of assessing clay desiccation for low rise buildings
In: *Proc Inst Civ Engrs*, vol 92, pp 82–89

CHANDLER, R J and FORSTER, A F (2001)
Engineering in Mercia Mudstone
C570, CIRIA, London

CHAPMAN, T J P, CONNOLLY, M L, NICHOLSON, D P, RAISON, C A and YEOW, H C (1999)
Advances in understanding of base grouted pile performance in very dense sand
In: *Proc symp tunnel construction and piling 99, London*

CHOW, F C, JARDINE, R J, NAUROY, J F and BRUCY, F (1997)
Time related increases in the shaft capabilities of driven piles in sand
Géotechnique, vol 47, no 2, pp 353–361

CLAYTON, C R I (1995)
The standard penetration test (SPT): methods and use
Report 143, CIRIA, London, 144 pp

CURTIS, D J (1976)
Discussion on "Circular tunnel in elastic ground"
Géotechnique, vol 26, pp 231–237

DAVIES, H and COUTTS, A W P (1994)
Planning and design of tunnels for the Jubilee Line Extension. Tunnelling 1994
Institution of Mining and Metallurgy, London

DAWSON, M P, DOUGLAS, A R, LINNEY, L, FRIEDMAN, M and ABRAHAM, R (1996)
Jubilee line extension, Bermondsey station box, design modifications, instrumentation and monitoring
In: *Proc int symp geotechnical aspects of underground construction in soft ground, City University, London*, AA Balkema, Rotterdam

DE MOOR, E K and STEVENSON, M C (1996)
Evaluation of the performance of a multi-propped diaphragm wall during construction
In: *Proc int symp geotechnical aspects of underground construction in soft ground, City University, London*, AA Balkema, Rotterdam, pp 111–116

DEWEY, H, BROMEHEAD, C E N, CHATWIN, C P and DINES, H G (1924)
The geology of the country around Dartford
Memoirs of the Geological Survey, Sheet 271, HMSO, London

DUPUIS, C and GRUAS-CAVAGNETTO, C (1996)
The Woolwich Beds and London Clay of Newhaven (East Sussex): new palynological and stratigraphical data
The London naturalist, no 75, pp 27–39

EDWARDS, R A and FRESHNEY, E C (1987a)
Geology of the country around Southampton
Memoir of the British Geological Survey, Sheet E315, HMSO, London

EDWARDS, R A and FRESHNEY, E C (1987b)
Lithostratigraphical classification of the Hampshire Basin Palaeogene deposits (Reading Formation to Hendon Formation)
Tertiary research, vol 8, pp 43–73

ELLISON, R A (1983)
Facies distribution in the Woolwich and Reading Beds of the London Basin, England
Proc Geologists' Association, vol 94, pp 311–319

ELLISON, R A (1991)
Lithostratigraphy of the Woolwich and Reading Beds along the proposed Jubilee Line Extension, south-east London
Unpublished Technical Report WA/91/5C to London Underground Ltd. British Geological Survey, Keyworth

ELLISON, R A, KNOX, R W O'B, JOLLEY, D W and KING, C (1994)
A revision of the lithostratigraphical classification of the early Palaeogene strata of the London Basin and East Anglia
In: *Proc Geologists' Association*, vol 105, pp 187–197

ELLISON, R A and LAKE, R D (1986)
Geology of the country around Braintree
Memoir of the British Geological Survey, Sheet E223, HMSO, London

ENVIRONMENT AGENCY (1997)
Rising groundwater levels in the Chalk-Basal Sands aquifer of the Central London Basin
Environment Agency, Thames Region

FARROW, J P and CLAYE, P M (1994)
Civil engineering and tunnel design
In: *Proc Inst Civ Engrs*, *Civ engg*, Thames Water Ring Main, pp 23–33

FOLLENFANT, H G, CUTHBERT, E W, MORGAN, H D, BARTLETT, J V, CLARK, J A M, HOOK, G S, LEE, J J, MASON, P L, THOMAS, D G and BUBBERS, B L (1969)
The Victoria Line
In: *Proc Inst Civ Engrs*, pp 337–475

GABA, A R (1989)
Instrumented driven steel tube piles at Canary Wharf, London
In: *Proc 3rd int conf piling and deep foundations*, London, vol 1, pp 337–346

GANNON, J A, MASTERTON, G G T, WALLACE, W A and MUIR WOOD, D (1999)
Piled foundations in weak rock
Report 181, CIRIA, London, 139 pp

GEORGIANNOU, V N, HIGHT, D W and BURLAND, J B (1993)
The behaviour of two hard clays in direct shear.
In: *Proc int conf geotechnical engineering in hard soils and soft rocks*, Athens, vol 1, pp 501–507

GIBSON, R E and ANDERSON, W F (1961)
In-situ measurements of soil properties with the pressuremeter
Civil engineering public works review, vol 56, no 658, May, pp 615–618

GILKES, R J (1968)
Clay mineral provinces in the Tertiary sediments of the Hampshire Basin
Clay minerals, vol 7, pp 351–361

GLASS, P R and POWDERHAM, A J (1994)
Application of the observational method at the Limehouse Link
Géotechnique, vol 44, no 4, pp 665–679

HARDING, H (1981)
Tunnelling history and my own involvement
Golder Associates, Toronto, 258 pp

HEPTON, P (1996)
Deep rotary cored boreholes in soils using wireline drilling
In: *Proc int conf advances in site investigation practice*, Thomas Telford, London,
pp 269–280

HESTER, S W (1965)
Stratigraphy and palaeography of the Woolwich and Reading Beds
Bulletin of the Geological Survey Great Britain, vol 23, pp 117–137

HIGHT, D W, BENNELL, J D, CHANA, B, DAVIS, P D, JARDINE, R J and
POROVIC, E (1997)
Wave velocity and stiffness measurements of the Crag and Lower Tertiaries at Sizewell
Géotechnique, vol 47, no 3, pp 451–474

HIGHT, D W and JARDINE, R J (1993)
Small strain stiffness and strength characteristics of hard London Tertiary clays
In: *Proc int conf geotechnical engineering in hard soils and soft rocks, Athens*

HUTCHINSON, J N (1980)
Possible late Quaternary pingo remnants in central London.
Nature, vol 284, pp 253–255

KELL, J and RIDLEY, G (1966)
Blackwall Tunnel duplication
In: *Proc Inst Civ Engrs*, pp 537–555

KLAASEN, H M (1883)
On a section of the Lower London Tertiaries at Park Hill, Croydon
In: *Proc Geologists' Association*, vol 8, pp 226–254

KNOX, R W O'B, MORIGI, A N, ALI, J R, HAILWOOD, E A and HALLAM, J R (1990)
Early Palaeogene stratigraphy of a cored borehole at Hales, Norfolk
In: *Proc Geologists' Association*, vol 101, pp 145–152

LEHANE, B M, PAUL, T S, CHAPMAN, T J P and JOHNSON, J G A (1995)
The apparent variability of the Woolwich and Reading Beds
In: *Proc XIth ECSMFE, Copenhagen*

LEWIS, J D and HARRIS, J R (in preparation)
The engineering implications of deoxygenated gases in the Lambeth Group of north
east London: a case history
Presentation, CIRIA seminar on the Lambeth Group, London, Oct 1998

LINNEY, L F and PAGE, D P (1996)
Site investigations for the tunnels and stations of the Jubilee Line Extension, London
In: *Proc int symp geotechnical aspects of underground construction in soft ground, City
University, London*, AA Balkema, Rotterdam, pp 779–784

LINNEY, L F and WITHERS, A D (1998)
Dewatering the Thanet Beds in SE London: three case histories
Q J engineering geology, vol 31, pp 115–122

LORD, J A, CLAYTON, C R I and MORTIMORE, R N (2002)
Engineering in chalk
C574, CIRIA, London

LORD, J A, TWINE, D and YEOW, H (1994)
Foundations in chalk
Project Report 11, CIRIA, London

LUCAS, H C and ROBINSON, V K (1995)
Modelling of rising groundwater levels in the Chalk aquifer of the London Basin
Q J engineering geology, vol 28, pp S51–62

MAIR, R J (1999)
Recent developments in geotechnical engineering in tunnelling
Harding Lectures, British Tunnelling Society

MAIR, R J, CHUDLEIGH, L J and TEDD, P (1997)
Geotechnical aspects of the reconstruction of London Underground's Angel station
Recommendations of the ERTC-9

MAIR, R J and TAYLOR, R N (1993)
Predictions of clay behaviour around tunnels using plasticity solutions
In: *Proc Wroth memorial symp: predictive soil mechanics, Oxford, 1992*, Thomas
Telford, London, pp 449–463

MAIR, R J, TAYLOR, R N and BURLAND, J B (1996)
Prediction of ground movements and assessment of risk of building damage due to
bored tunnelling
In: *Proc int symp geotechnical aspects of underground construction in soft ground, City
University, London*, AA Balkema, Rotterdam

MARSLAND, A (1971)
The use of *in situ* tests in a study of the effects of fissures on the properties of stiff
fissured clays
In: *Proc 1st Australian-New Zealand conf on geomechanics, Melbourne, Aug*, vol 1,
pp 180–189

MATHER, N E E (1986)
Acid groundwater attack on a section of London Underground's tunnels between
Moorgate and Old Street stations
Unpublished MSc dissertation, University of London

MATHEWSON, A and LAVAL, D (1992)
Brunel's tunnel and where it led
Brunel Exhibition, Rotherhithe, London, 68 pp

McDOWELL, P (1989)
Ground subsidence associated with doline formation in chalk areas of Southern England.
In: *Proc 3rd multidisciplinary conf on sinkholes, St Petersburg, Florida*

McINNES, R G, JEWELL, S and ROBERTS, H (1998)
Coastal management of the Isle of Wight, UK
The geographical journal, vol 64, pp 291–306

MEASOR, E O and WILLIAMS, G M J (1958)
Features in the design and construction of the Shell Centre
In: *Proc Inst Civ Engrs*, pp 475–501

MORIARTY, J M and COOPER, M L (1991)
Reconstruction of London Underground's Angel station
In: *Proc Tunnelling '91, Institution of Mining and Metallurgy, London*, pp 233–248

MORTON, K and AU, E (1974)
Settlement observation on eight structures in London
In: *Settlement of structures*, Pentech Press, pp 183–203

MUIR WOOD, A M (1975)
Circular tunnel in elastic ground
Géotechnique, vol 25, no 1, pp 115–127

MUIR WOOD, A M (1994)
The Thames Tunnel 1825–43: where shield tunnelling began
In: *Proc Inst Civ Engrs, Civ engg*, vol 102, pp 130–139

O'RIORDAN, N J (1982)
The mobilisation of shaft adhesion down a bored cast-*in-situ* pile in the Woolwich and Reading beds
Ground engineering, April, pp 17–26

PAGE, D P (1994)
The engineering geology of the Lambeth Group
MSc thesis, University of Surrey

PAGE, D P (in preparation)
Patterns of slope instability in the Lambeth Group

PAGE, D P and SKIPPER, J A E (2000)
Lithological characteristics of the Lambeth Group
Ground engineering, vol 33, no 2, pp 38–43

PALMER, A C (1972)
Undrained plane-strain expansion of a cylindrical cavity in clay: a simple interpretation of the pressuremeter test
Géotechnique, vol 22, no 3, Sep, pp 451–457

PERRY, J (1989)
A survey of slope condition on motorway earthworks in England and Wales
Research Report RR199. Transport Research Laboratory, Crowthorne

PERRY, J (1991)
The extent and an analysis of shallow failures on the slopes of highway earthworks
PhD thesis, University of Durham

PERRY, J (1995)
Engineering geology of soils in highway construction: a general overview
In: M Eddleston, S Walthall, J C Cripps and M G Culshaw (eds) *Engineering geology of construction*
Geological Society Special Publication no 10, pp 189–203

PICKLES, A and EVERTON, S (1996)
Aspects of the site investigation for the Waterloo International Terminal
In: *Proc int conf advances in site investigation practice*
Thomas Telford, London, pp 1–12

POTTS, D M and ADDENBROOKE, T I (1996)
The influence of existing surface structure on the ground movements due to tunnelling
In: *Proc int symp geotechnical aspects of underground construction in soft ground, City University, London*, AA Balkema, Rotterdam

PREENE, M and POWRIE, W (1993)
Steady-state performance of construction dewatering systems in fine soils
Géotechnique, vol 43, no 2, pp 191–205

PREENE, M and ROBERTS, T O L (in preparation)
Groundwater control for construction in the Lambeth Group
Presentation, CIRIA seminar on the Lambeth Group, London, Oct 1998

PRESTWICH, J (1854)
On the structure of the strata between the London Clay and the Chalk in the London and Hampshire Tertiary systems. Part II. The Woolwich and Reading Series
Q J Geological Society of London, vol 10, pp 75–138

PULLER, M J and PULLER, D J (1993)
Developments in structural slurry walls. Retaining structures
Thomas Telford, London, pp 373–384

RAINEY, T P and ROSENBAUM, M S (1989)
The adverse influence of geology and ground water on the behaviour of London Underground railway tunnels near Old Street station
In: *Proc Geological Association*, vol 100, pp 123–134

REID, C (1898)
The geology of the country around Bournemouth.
Memoir of the Geological Survey of Great Britain, Sheet 329

REID, C (1902)
The geology of the country around Southampton.
Memoir of the Geological Survey of Great Britain, Sheet 315

RENNIE, G (1846)
Note accompanying a specimen of a calcareous band in the plastic Clay from the bed of the Thames
Q J Geological Society, vol 2, p 260

RHODES, S J and MARYCHURCH, I M (1998)
Chalk solution features at three sites in south-east England: their formation and treatment
In: J G Maund, and M Eddleston (eds) *Geohazards in engineering geology*
Engineering Geology Special Publication no 15, Geological Society, London, pp 277–289

RIDEHALGH, H (1958)
Shoreham Harbour development.
In: *Proc Inst Civ Engrs*, vol 2, pp 285–298

ROBINS, N S, KINNIBURGH, D G and BIRD, M J (1997)
Generation of acid groundwater beneath City Road, London.
In: *Proc int conf implications of ground chemistry and microbiology for construction, Univ Bristol, 1992*, AA Balkema, Rotterdam

SCARROW, J A and GOSLING, R C (1986)
An example of rotary core drilling in soils
In: *Site investigation practice: assessing BS5930*, Geol Soc Engineering Geology
Special Publication no 2, pp 357–363

SIMPSON, B, CALABRESI, G, SOMMER, H and WALLAYS, M (1979)
Design parameters for stiff clays. General report
In: *Proc 7th Euro conf soil mechanics and foundation engineering*, vol 5, pp 91–125

SIMPSON, B, BLOWER, T, CRAIG, R N and WILKINSON, W B (1989)
*The engineering implications of rising groundwater levels in the deep aquifer beneath
London*
Special Publication 69, CIRIA, London

SKEMPTON, A W (1977)
Slope stability of cuttings in brown London Clay
In: *Proc 9th int conf soil mechanics and foundation engineering, Tokyo*, Japanese
Society of Soil Mechanics and Foundation Engineering, vol 3, pp 261–270

SKEMPTON, A W and CHRIMES, M M (1994)
Thames Tunnel: geology, site investigation and geotechnical problems
Géotechnique, vol 44, no 2, pp 191–216

SKEMPTON, A W and HENKEL, D J (1957)
Tests on London Clay from deep borings at Paddington, Victoria and the South Bank
In: *Proc 4th in conf soil mechanics and foundation engineering*, vol 1, pp 100–106

SOLERA, S A (1998)
Continuous flight auger piles in the Woolwich and Reading Beds in the Isle of Dogs,
London
In: *Proc 7th int conf piling and deep foundations, Vienna*, DFI paper 1.9

SPINK, T W (1991)
Periglacial discontinuities in Eocene Clays near Denham Bucks
In: A Forster, M G Culshaw, J C Cripps, J A Little and C F Moon (eds), *Quaternary
engineering geology*, Geol Soc Engineering Geology Special Publication no 7, Edinburgh,
pp 389–396

ST JOHN, H D (1975)
Field and theoretical studies of the behaviour of ground around deep excavations in
London Clay
PhD thesis, Cambridge University Department of Engineering

STEGER, E H and DERBYSHIRE, P H (1975)
Piling onto Thanet Sand at Euston Square
Ground engineering, vol 8, no 5, Sep, pp 29–33

STEVENSON, M C and DE MOOR, E K (1994)
Limehouse Link cut and cover tunnel: design and performance
In: *Proc 8th int conf soil mechanics and foundation engineering, New Delhi*

TRENTER, N A (1999)
Engineering in glacial tills
C504, CIRIA, London, 259 pp

TROUGHTON, V M (1992)
The design and performance of foundations for the Canary Wharf development in London Docklands
Géotechnique, vol 42, no 3, pp 381–393

TROUGHTON, V M AND PLATIS, A (1989)
The effects of changes in effective stress on a base grouted pile in sand
In: *Proc 3rd int conf piling and deep foundations, London*, vol 1, pp 445–453

VAUGHAN, P R and WALBANCKE, H J (1973)
Pore pressure changes and the delayed failure of cutting slopes in overconsolidated clay
Géotechnique, vol 23, pp 531–539

WARD, W H (1947)
A coastal landslip
In: *Proc 1st int conf soil mechanics and foundation engineering*, vol 2, pp 33–38

WATER RESOURCES BOARD (1972)
The hydrogeology of the London Basin
Water Resources Board, Reading

WEST, G (1988)
Innovation and the rise of the tunnelling industry
Cambridge University Press, 349 pp

WHITAKER, W (1872)
The geology of the London Basin. Part I. The Chalk and the Eocene beds of the southern and western tracts
Memoir of the Geological Survey of England and Wales

WHITTAKER, A, HOLLIDAY, D W and PENN, I E (1985)
Geophysical logs in British stratigraphy
Geological Society Special Report no 18

WILLIAMS, G M J (1957)
Design of the foundations of the Shell Building, London
In: *Proc 4th int conf soil mechanics and foundation engineering*, vol 1, pp 457–461

YEATS, J A AND O'RIORDAN, N J (1989)
The design and construction of large diameter base grouted piles in the Thanet Sand at Blackwall Yard, London
In: *Proc 3rd int conf piling and deep foundations*, London, vol 1, pp 455–461

A1   Bibliography

A1.1   MEMOIRS OF THE BRITISH GEOLOGICAL SURVEY

BLAKE, J H and MONCKTON, H W (1903)
The geology of the country around Reading
Sheet 268, HMSO, London

BOSWELL, P G H (1927)
The geology of the country around Ipswich. Explanation of sheet 207
HMSO, London

BRISTOW, C R (1985)
Geology of the country around Chelmsford
Sheet E241, HMSO, London

BRISTOW, C R; FRESHNEY, E C and PENN, I E (1991)
Geology of the country around Bournemouth
Sheet E329, HMSO, London

DEWEY, H and BROMEHEAD, C E N (1915)
The geology of the country around Windsor and Chertsey
Sheet 269, HMSO, London

DEWEY, H and BROMEHEAD, C E N (1921)
The geology of the country around South London
Sheet 270, HMSO, London

DEWEY, H, BROMEHEAD, C E N, CHATWIN, C P and DINES, H G (1924)
The geology of the country around Dartford
Sheet 271, HMSO, London

DINES, H G and EDMUNDS, F H (1925)
The geology of the country around Romford
Sheet 257, HMSO, London

EDWARDS, R A and FRESHNEY, E C (1987)
Geology of the country around Southampton
Sheet E315, HMSO, London

ELLISON, R A and LAKE, R D (1986)
Geology of the country around Braintree
Sheet E223, HMSO, London

HOLMES, S C A (1981)
Geology of the country around Faversham
Sheet E273, HMSO, London

LAKE, R D, ELLISON, R A, HENSON, M R and CONWAY, B W (1986)
Geology of the country around Southend and Foulness
Sheets E258 and E259, HMSO, London

LAKE, R D and WILSON, D (1990)
Geology of the country around Great Dunmow
Sheet E222, HMSO, London

MILLWARD, D, ELLISON, R A, LAKE, R D and MOORLOCK, B S P M (1987)
Geology of the country around Epping
Sheet E240, HMSO, London, 80 pp

REID, C (1898)
The geology of the country around Bournemouth
Sheet 329, HMSO, London

REID, C (1902)
The geology of the country around Southampton
Sheet 315, HMSO, London

SHEPHARD-THORN, E R (1988)
The geology of the country around Ramsgate and Dover
Sheets E274 and E290, HMSO, London

SHERLOCK, R L and NOBLE, A H (1922)
The geology of the country around Beaconsfield
Sheet 255, HMSO, London

SHERLOCK, R L and POCOCK, R W (1924)
The geology of the country around Hertford
Sheet 239, HMSO, London

SMART, J G O; BISSON, G and WORSSAM, B C (1966)
The geology of the country around Canterbury and Folkestone
Sheets E289, E305 and E306, HMSO, London

WHITAKER, W (1872)
The geology of the London Basin. Part I. The Chalk and the Eocene beds of the southern and western tracts

WHITE, H J O (1907)
The geology of the country around Hungerford and Newbury
Sheet 267, HMSO, London

WHITE, H J O (1909)
The geology of the country around Basingstoke
Sheet 284, HMSO, London

WHITE, H J O (1910)
The geology of the country around Alresford
Sheet 300, HMSO, London

WHITE, H J O (1912)
The geology of the country near Lymington and Portsmouth
Sheet 330 and 331, HMSO, London

WHITE, H J O (1913)
The geology of the country near Fareham and Havant
Sheet 316, HMSO, London

WHITE, H J O (1915)
The geology of the country near Lymington and Portsmouth
Sheets 330 and 331, HMSO, London

WHITE, H J O (1921)
A short account of the geology of the Isle of Wight
HMSO, London

WHITE, H J O (1925)
The geology of the country around Marlborough
Sheet 266, HMSO, London

A1.2   OTHER REFERENCES

BONE, D A (1989)
Temporary exposures in the Lower Palaeogene of the eastern Hampshire Basin
(Chichester to Havant)
In: *Proc Geological Association*, vol 100, pp 147–159

COX, F C, HAILWOOD, E A, HARLAND, R, HUGHES, M, JOHNSTON, N and
KNOX, R W O'B (1985)
Palaeocene sedimentation and stratigraphy in Norfolk, England
Newsletters on stratigraphy, vol 14, no 3, pp 169–185

HALLSWORTH, C (1994)
*Stratigraphical variations in the heavy minerals of the Palaeogene sandstones in the
London Basin, and the implications for sand provenance*
Technical Report WH/93/288R, British Geological Survey, Keyworth

HEPWORTH, J V (1998)
Aspects of the English silcretes and comparison with some Australian occurrences
In: *Proc Geologists' Association*, vol 109, pp 271–288

KNOX, R W O'B and MORTON, A C (1988)
The record of early Tertiary N. Atlantic volcanism in sediments of the North Sea Basin
In: A C Morton and L M Parson (eds), *Early Tertiary volcanism*, Special Publication
no 39, Geological Society of London

MOORLOCK, B S P and HIGHLEY, D E (1991)
An appraisal of fuller's earth resources in England and Wales
Technical Report WA/91/75, British Geological Survey, Keyworth, 85 pp

MORTON, A C (1982)
Heavy minerals of Hampshire Basin Palaeogene strata
Geological magazine, vol 119, pp 463–476

SUMMERFIELD, M A and GOUDIE, A S (1980)
The sarsens of southern England: their palaeoenvironment interpretation with reference
to other silcretes
In: D H C Jones (ed), *The shaping of southern England*, Academic Press, London

ULLYOTT, J S, NASH, D J and SHAW, P A (1998)
Recent advances in silcrete research and their implications for the origin and
palaeoenvironmental significance of sarsens
In: *Proc Geologists' Association*, vol 109, pp 255–270

WEIR, A H and CATT, A J (1968)
The mineralogy of Palaeogene sediments in northeast Kent (Great Britain)
Sedimentary geology, vol 3, pp 17–33

WHITTAKER, A, HOLLIDAY, D W and PENN, I E (1985)
Geophysical logs in British stratigraphy
Geological Society Special Report no 18

A2 Photographs of cores and exposures of the Lambeth Group

The boundaries between the units are as follows:

Base of London Clay 23.64 m; base of Harwich Formation (Blackheath Beds) 24.11 m; base of Upper Shelly Clay 25.05 m; base of Upper Mottled Clay 29.63 m

Base of Laminated beds 33.16 m; base of Lower Shelly Clay 33.77 m; base of Lower Mottled Clay 35.15 m; base of Upnor Formation 41.13 m

Figure A2.1 *Lambeth Group core photographs of Jubilee Line Extension borehole 404T*

The boundaries between the units are as follows:

Base of London Clay 23.64 m; base of Harwich Formation (Blackheath Beds) 24.11 m; base of Upper Shelly Clay 25.05 m; base of Upper Mottled Clay 29.63 m

Base of Laminated beds 33.16 m; base of Lower Shelly Clay 33.77 m; base of Lower Mottled Clay 35.15 m; base of Upnor Formation 41.13 m

Figure A2.1 *Lambeth Group core photographs of Jubilee Line Extension borehole 404T (continued)*

The following figures show Lambeth Group exposures.

Figure A2.2 *Detail of the Laminated beds in JLE borehole 305T*

Figure A2.3 *Detail of boundary between Lower Shelly Clay and Lower Mottled; arrow points to top of succession Clay in JLE borehole 305T. Note the burrows filled with dark grey Lower Shelly Clay within Lower Mottled Clay*

Figure A2.4   *Lower Shelly Clay at Upnor Quarry, north Kent [TQ 759711]*

Figure A2.5   *Detail of Lower Shelly Clay at Upnor Quarry*

Figure A2.6   *General view of the Lambeth Group at Upnor Quarry.*
Thinly bedded dark grey beds are Lower Shelly Clay; pale grey sands with brown
ferruginous layers are the local equivalent of the Lower Mottled Clay; pale bedded
sands that constitute the lower part of the succession are the Upnor Formation

Figure A2.7   *Section at Orsett Cock Quarry [TQ 657810].*
Ferruginous terrace gravels overlie well-bedded pale grey sand and thin grey clay
seams with a thick cross-stratified pebble bed (Upnor Formation pebble bed)

Figure A2.8   *General view of Lambeth Group at Upnor Quarry (explanation as for Figure A2.6)*

A3 Case history data

Table A3.1 Summary of major case history data for tunnels constructed within the Lambeth Group (adapted from Page, 1994)

No	Project	Location	Date	Excavation/support method	Strata encountered	Difficulties experienced	Result
1	Thames Driftway (Vazie – Trevithick)	Rotherhithe to Limehouse	1805–1808	Hand-dug timber heading	LMC/Upnor Formation (upper).	Insufficient clay cover (LSC). Ground loss of sands from Lb.	Tunnel abandoned 315 m from Rotherhithe shaft.
2	Thames Tunnel (Sir Marc Brunel)	Rotherhithe to Wapping	1825–1843	Hand-dug using compartmentalised cast iron shield. Brick-lined.	UMC, Lb, LSC, LMC, Upnor Formation (upper)	Five inflows of the river, numerous collapses. Shield damaged.	Tunnel delayed. Loss of sponsorship. Loss of life.
3	Greenwich Foot Tunnel	Greenwich to Isle of Dogs (Island Gardens)					
4	Blackwall Tunnel (1)	North Greenwich to Blackwall	1891–1897	Hand-dug shield. Cast iron lining. Compressed air.	Basal LC, Lb, LSC, LMC, Upnor Formation (upper) + TG filled "scour feature".	Difficult excavation (LMC – duricrust). Shield damaged (LMC – duricrust).	Tunnel delayed.
5	Rotherhithe Tunnel	Rotherhithe to Shadwell	1904–1908	Price rotary digger shield used for pilot tunnel. Enlarged by hand in compressed air (14–20 psi). Cast iron lining.	UMC, LSC, LMC (+duricrust), Upnor Formation (including pebble bed)		
6	Northern Line	Euston Station to Charing Cross	1901 and 1920	Compressed air.	UMC with channel sand bodies		

Table A3.1 *Summary of major case history data for tunnels constructed within the Lambeth Group (adapted from Page, 1994)* (continued)

No	Project	Location	Date	Excavation/support method	Strata encountered	Difficulties experienced	Result
7	Central Line	Bond Street to St Paul's	1897				
8	Central Line Extension (Ilford)	Stratford Station to Leyton	1930s	Compressed air @ 5 lb psi.	LSC, UF (pebble bed).		
9	Central Line Extension (Ilford)	Whitechapel to Stratford Station		Compressed air @ 25 lb psi.	Lb, UMC, USC (?HF), LC.	Fine sand and silt of the Lb sensitive to air pressures.	
10	Blackwall Tunnel (2)	North Greenwich to Blackwall	1966	Two hand-dug shields enlarged from pilot tunnel in chemically grouted Lb under compressed air. Cast iron lining.	Basal LC, Lb, LMC, Upnor Formation + TG filled scour feature.	Lb silica and resin grouted to reduce permeability from two pilot tunnels.	
11	Victoria Line	Walthamstow to Brixton	1967–1971	Combination of mechanical shields and open face TBMs. Hand mining. Expanded PCC, bolted PCC and cast iron. Grommetted bolts and gaskets.	LC predominantly. UMC at Euston and Warren Street Stations.	Dewatered using standpipes from pilot tunnels. Resin grouting from the surface.	Six-month delay on Euston station.
12	Jubilee Line	Baker St to Charing Cross	1971–1976	Mechanical shields. Expanded PCC and bolted cast iron in LG	LC predominantly. LG towards Baker St and Bond St.	Falls of ground in build area of TBMs. Difficulties in controlling shield. Swelling of clay.	Trailing fingers added to tailskin.
13	Thames Water Ring Main	Streatham to Brixton	1987–1989	Open face shields with compressed air. PCC bolted segments with compression gaskets.	LC, LG (1.8 km), TSF (1 km from Tooting Bec to Radbourne Road)	Drilling an exploratory hole from tunnel invert into the underlying TSF caused inundation of the tunnel.	Emergency access shaft constructed to recover shield using ground freezing. Drive completed using EPBM.
14	Thames Water Ring Main	Park Lane to Barrow Hill (2.5 km)	1988–1990	Sectionalised backhoe and extended backhoe with compressed air. PCC bolted lining.	Detailed geology not described.		
15	Thames Water Ring Main	Barrow Hill to New River Head (3.3 km)	1990	EPBM with PCC bolted segments (trapezoidal).	Ditto	None	Drive completed in open mode.

Table A3.1 *Summary of major case history data for tunnels constructed within the Lambeth Group (adapted from Page, 1994) (continued)*

No	Project	Location	Date	Excavation/support method	Strata encountered	Difficulties experienced	Result
16	Thames Water Ring Main	Stoke Newington to Coppermills (2 km)	1987–1989	Open face shield fitted with roadheader with PCC bolted segments and pipejack lining	Ditto	Water-bearing sand lenses.	1.5 km in pipejack remainder in compressed air due to presence of sand lens.
17	Three Valleys Tunnel	Wraysbury Reservoir to Iver Water	1984–1986	Open face shield with backhoe. PCC bolted switch from expanded lining.	Predominantly LC, but LG over. Pingo disturbing TSF, LG, LC and TG.	Impersistent 600 mm-thick band of siltstone at base of LC. Water-bearing pebble bed sloughing in build area for which expanded lining inappropriate. Pingo had created highly disturbed ground.	Compressed air (0.7 bar) used and lining changed to PCC bolted though LG. Permeation grouting of silty sands using combination of cement/bentonite and chemical grout within pingo failed. Recourse to ground freezing. Significant costs and delays.
18	Angel Station (Northern Line)	Angel, Islington	1989–1991	Hand-dug. Bolted SGI lining.	LC, station tunnels drive in 50% UMC, 50% LC.	Difficult to determine if interface would be water-bearing.	None.
19	Royal Docks Drainage	Royal Docks	1984–1991	Nine drives in LG. EPBM, slurry shields and open face TBMs. Pipejacks and PCC bolted segments.	LG (sub-units not specified), TSF.	Variable jacking pressures, clogging of slurry shields, loss of vertical alignment. Rock (duricrust), present in four drives. Distortion of TBM tailskin due to high ground loads.	Abandonment of one drive and re-drive.
20	Northern Line	Old St to Moorgate	1962–1995	Bolted cast iron lining constructed in 1901 and 1922–4. Replaced with bolted stainless steel lining 1995.	Basal LC, UMC.	Deformation and cracking of existing tunnel lining.	Remedial measures have included strapping and bracing. Lining replaced in 1995.
21	Jubilee Line Extension – Contract 104	London Bridge Station	1994–1997	Roadheader/backhoe lined using shotcrete support method.	LC, UMC.		

Table A3.1 *Summary of major case history data for tunnels constructed within the Lambeth Group (adapted from Page, 1994)* (continued)

No	Project	Location	Date	Excavation/support method	Strata encountered	Difficulties experienced	Result
22	Jubilee Line Extension – Contract 105	Bermondsey to Canada Water	1994–1997	EPBM, lined with PCC bolted segments. Compressed air for station enlargement at Bermondsey beneath grouted TG.	LC, Lambeth Group, TSF.	Delay attributed to difficulty in selecting appropriate spoil conditioner.	
23	Jubilee Line Extension – Contract 107	Canada Water to Canary Wharf	1994–1997	Slurry machine lined with PCC bolted segments.	TSF, Lambeth Group.	Hydrocyclones required to condition slurry by removing silt fraction.	
24	Jubilee Line Extension – Contract 110	Canary Wharf to Canning Town	1994–1997	EPBM (closed and open modes) lined with PCC bolted segments.	LC, Lambeth Group.		
25	Docklands Light Railway Lewisham Extension	Isle of Dogs (Island Gardens) to Greenwich	1997–1999	Slurry machine lined with PCC bolted segments. Cross-passage constructed under compressed air.	Lambeth Group, TSF.		
26	Portsmouth to Havant Waste Water Transfer Tunnel	Havant to Portsmouth (Langstone Harbour)	1998–2002	Lovat EPBM.	Lambeth Group, LC, Chalk, Bracklesham Beds.		

Key

TG = Terrace Gravel	Lb = Laminated beds
LC = London Clay	LSC = Lower Shelly Clay
HF = Harwich Formation	LMC = Lower Mottled Clay
LG = Lambeth Group	UF = Upnor Formation
UMC = Upper Mottled Clay	TSF = Thanet Sand Formation.

Table A3.2 *Summary of major case history data for shaft construction within the Lambeth Group*

No	Project	Location	Date	Excavation/support method	Strata encountered	Difficulties experienced	Result
1	Thames Tunnel – Rotherhithe Shaft	Rotherhithe, London		Brickwork caisson through drift then underlay through LG.	LG.	Groundwater control in UF.	Sheet piles extended down through UF to prevent base heave.
2	Blackwell Tunnel – Poplar Shaft	Poplar London		Concrete caisson – blowing down.	LG.		
3	Victoria Line	Euston		Two shafts. One in compressed air the other by jacking down.	Silty sand channel bodies within UMC.		
4	Royal Docks Drainage	Royal Docks, East London	1989	Wet caisson.	LG (unspecified).	Rock ledges.	Increase kentledge; use of wet chiselling equipment.
5	JLE	Prestons Road		Diaphragm walls.	TG, LG, TSF, Chalk.		
6	JLE	Durands Wharf		Wet caisson.	TG, LG, TSF, Chalk.	Rock ledges within the LG, dewatering of the lowermost part of the TSF.	Pre-excavation of LG by installation of slurry trench, caisson completed by blowing down under compressed air.
7	JLE	Old Jamaica Road		Diaphragm walls, slurry trench machine.		None.	

Key

TG = Terrace Gravel   Lb = Laminated beds
LC = London Clay   LSC = Lower Shelly Clay
HF = Harwich Formation   LMC = Lower Mottled Clay
LG = Lambeth Group   UF = Upnor Formation
UMC = Upper Mottled Clay   TSF = Thanet Sand Formation.

Table A3.3   *Summary of major case study data for deep excavations*

Project	Ground conditions	Retention system	Key conclusions
British Library, Euston Road	Predominantly LC, LG in base of excavation. 4 m in UMC (mottled clays).	119 no 1.8 m-diameter secant bored pile wall.	
Limehouse Link (1.8 km long, 1.6 km cut-and-cover tunnel linking the Canary Wharf development with the City)	TG, LC, LG and TSF. LG subdivided into five units A to E.	Top-down construction within diaphragm walls up to 33 m deep, penetrating up to 9 m into Thanet Sand Formation. Excavation span varies from 21 m to 42 m. Dewatering was achieved by pumping from the underlying Chalk and TSF. The Lb were dewatered by the use of downward-draining sand wicks.	Engineer's design based on established correlation for material properties since behaviour of deep excavations in the Lambeth Group is unknown. Contractor adopted observational method and value engineering to reduce temporary support requirements.
Bermondsey Station, Jubilee Line Extension	TG, LC, LG (USC, UMC, Lb, LSC, LMC, UF).	50 m × 45 m × 19.5 m-deep box constructed top-down within diaphragm walls constructed using rope-operated grabs. Dewatering was achieved by a combination of deep wells into the TSF, 4 within the box and 4 outside.	Higher stiffnesses were adopted by the contractor based on 0.1 per cent small strain triaxial testing which enabled the construction sequence to be simplified and a set of temporary props to be omitted.
Canada Water Station, Jubilee Line Extension	TG, LG (Lb, LSC, LMC, UF), TSF.	Bottom-up and top-down construction within secant bored pile wall. Tubular props and ground anchors used to support wall in temporary case.	Prop loads measured greatly influenced by temperature changes.

Key:

TG = Terrace Gravel
LC = London Clay
HF = Harwich Formation
LG = Lambeth Group
UMC = Upper Mottled Clay

Lb = Laminated beds
LSC = Lower Shelly Clay
LMC = Lower Mottled Clay
UF = Upnor Formation
TSF = Thanet Sand Formation.

Table A3.4 *Summary of key references on pile behaviour in the Lambeth Group*

Reference	Pile Types	Key conclusions
Steger, E H and Derbyshire, P H (1975). *Piling onto Thanet Sand at Euston Square*. Ground engineering, vol 8, no 5 September, pp 29–33. Stratigraphy: 3 m made ground, 16.5 m London Clay (very stiff mottled clay), 3.5 m Lambeth Sand (yellow and white sand), 2.5 m Upnor Clay? (very hard mottled green clay), 0.8 m gravel in silt matrix, 5 m Thanet Sand. No details on effective stress conditions were given.	Bored, cast *in situ*. Three buildings had 0.75–1.8 m shaft diameter under-reamed piles founded 0.5 m into the top of the Lambeth Clay. One building with higher loads used 1.2 m and 1.5 m-diameter straight-shafted piles founded 1 m into the Thanet Sand. Two trial piles, 0.75 m diameter, were constructed, one founded in Lambeth Sand (yellow and white) and lined through the London Clay, one founded in the Thanet Sand and lined over the upper 34.5 m.	Multi-storey office blocks at Euston Square, London. Trials showed that bores into the Thanet Sand could be drilled dry with sections through the Lambeth deposits (reportedly containing bands of wet sand) remaining stable for a few hours. Despite this, piles were bored with bentonite to reduce the risks of bore instability, base disturbance, base heave, problems due to delays in concreting and to allow the placement of concrete through a tremie providing better quality than free-fall concreting. The instrumented trial piles were constructed over several days. Static load testes showed that the pile founded in the Lambeth Sand reached a load of 8000 kN after 70 mm displacement while the pile in the Thanet Sand reached 8800 kN after 80 mm displacement. The load-displacement curves do not allow the easy separation of shaft and base loads though the first pile was inferred to have an estimated shaft load of about 2000 kN. This corresponds to an average shaft friction through the Lambeth Clay and Lambeth Sand of $f_s = 66$ kPa and a base resistance of 13.6 MPa with $N_q = 30$ to 42.
St John, H D (1975). *Field and theoretical studies of the behaviour of ground around deep excavations in London Clay*. PhD thesis, Cambridge University. YMCA stratigraphy: 7 m fill and gravel, 18.5 m London Clay, very stiff Lambeth Clay.	Bored cast *in situ* piles with under-reams constructed dry in the top of the Lambeth Clay taking column loads of around 25 MN. 2 m diameter with 5 m under-reams, some constructed at 1:25 rakes to avoid overlapping.	Piles founded in the London Clay would not have been of sufficient capacity. A 1 m-diameter inspection shaft was sunk to allow the Lambeth strata to be inspected visually. No water-bearing strata or sand layers were detected. Plate bearing tests confirmed high stiffness and a bearing resistance of 1 MPa was used in the final design. Under-reamed piles were constructed without bentonite and there were no stability problems.
O'Riordan, N J (1982). *The mobilisation of shaft adhesion down a bored, cast-in-situ pile in the Woolwich and Reading Beds*. Ground engineering, vol 15, no 3, April, pp 17–26. Stratigraphy: 2 m fill, 18.5 m London Clay, 14.5 m Lambeth Clay, 5 m Lambeth Sand (partially saturated very hard greenish grey sandy clay with pockets of sand), 3.5 m Thanet Sand (dry), Chalk. Piezometer readings showed that pore pressures in the London Clay and Lambeth Clay were 60% of hydrostatic due to under-drainage in the Chalk. O'Riordan assumed that there was zero pore pressure in the Lambeth and Thanet Sands and this had been used in the current interpretation of effective stress design parameters.	Bored, cast *in situ* 1.53 m and 1.05 m-diameter piles founded in Lambeth Sand. 1.53 m-diameter pile was 38.5 m long and sleeved with the 13 m long unsleeved section through Lambeth Clay and 2 m of Lambeth Sand. Instrumented and with a polystyrene inclusion at the base so that the shaft capacity could be identified.	British Library, Euston Road, London. Piles were bored dry, ie without bentonite. A maintained load test was conducted on the 1.53 m-diameter pile with a final cycle at a constant rate of penetration to the maximum capacity of the reaction frame, 27 MN, causing a pile head displacement of 190 mm. A shaft capacity of about 9.15 MN was developed after a pile head displacement of about 4 mm with approximate shaft friction in the Lambeth Clay $f_s = 75$ to 113 kPa ($\alpha = 0.36$ to 0.4) and in the Lambeth Sand $f_s = 230$ kPa ($K = 0.47$), where: $f_s = \alpha c_u$ in clay with $c_u = 200$ to 280 kPa and $f_s = \sigma_v'K \tan$ in sand with $\varphi' = 33°$. It should be noted that drained shear box tests gave residual angles of friction of 13° in the Lambeth Clay and 22° in the Lambeth Sand. The 1.05 m-diameter pile was sleeved along its entire length in order to measure base resistance alone. Both piles indicated ultimate base resistances of about 10.7 MPa, equivalent to $N_q = 14$. This relatively low N_q value, developed after a large pile displacement, may be indicative of base disturbance, the presence of loose or clayey material at the base or base heave during boring which was conducted dry.

Table A3.4 *Summary of key references on pile behaviour in the Lambeth Group (continued)*

Reference	Pile types	Key conclusions
Troughton, V M (1992). The design and performance of foundations for the Canary Wharf development in London Docklands. *Géotechnique*, vol 42, no 3, pp 381–393. Generalised stratigraphy: Ground level approx + 5 m OD, 4 m fill and alluvium, 7 m Terrace Gravel, 8 m Lambeth Clay (cemented pebble layer, then shell beds interleaved with mottled clays, intermittent limestone and calcareous nodules towards the base), 5 m Lambeth Sand (sandy clay with a bottom bed of glauconitic sands and pebbles with blue and black clays), 16 m Thanet Sand, 100 m + Chalk. Underdrainage in the Chalk results in a lower aquifer with piezometric level at -5 m OD.	Driven steel tubes for foundations over water (also described by Gaba, 1989). Base-grouted auger-bored piles for buildings on land. 1.5 m diameter founded in Thanet Sand. Driven precast piles for Westferry Circus car park. 350 mm square, driven in large groups at about 1.2 m centres, founded in the mottled sand below the Lambeth Clay. Bored piles for Westferry Circus 750 mm and 900 mm diameter. Continuous-flight auger piles (CFA), 600 mm-diameter settlement-reducing piles for the roadway. Also diaphragm walls and cofferdams in London Clay.	Dynamic tests on steel piles showed approximately 35 per cent increase in shaft resistance between installation and restrike, sometimes achieved within one day of driving. This was attributed to the dissipation of excess pore pressures in the Lambeth Clay, but could equally be due to increases in pile shaft capacity in the sand deposits, as described by Chow *et al* (1997). Auger-bored piles were constructed with a temporary casing sealing into the top of the Lambeth Clay to prevent water ingress from the overlying sand and gravel. A 1.2 m-diameter trial bore remained stable within the greater part of the Lambeth Clay but water seepages became significant from a gravel layer at the base of the Lambeth Group. Water was added in an attempt to balance the groundwater pressure, but was lost when the Thanet Sand was penetrated. Piles were constructed under bentonite into the Thanet Sand and base grouted. Precast piles were driven to a minimum set of 100 for 250 mm and minimum penetration of -14 m OD and were able to carry loads of up to 1500 kN with settlements of about 5 mm. Intermittent limestone caused the refusal of some piles, which were still acceptable due to their high end-bearing resistance. Driving of adjacent piles in a group caused a maximum pile uplift of 17 mm, but a load on this pile conformed to the specification of 10 mm settlement at working load. Thus, redriving was only needed for piles where uplift exceeded 17 mm. Bored piles founded in the Thanet Sand were used in areas with substantial masonry obstructions and adjacent to the sensitive brick dock wall where the driving vibrations from precast piles were undesirable. CFA piles were constructed in the Lambeth Group founded either on limestone band at or below -12 m OD (refusal) or in the Lambeth Sand at -14 m OD. Load deflection curves from static tests showed the pile founded on the limestone band displayed stiffer behaviour and indicated higher ultimate loads. At working loads of 1500 kN, both piles gave similar settlements.
Troughton, V M and Platis, A (1989). The effects of changes in effective stress on a base grouted pile in sand. *Proc 3rd int conf piling and deep foundations, London*, vol 1, pp 445–453. Stratigraphy: 6 m fill and alluvium, 6 m Terrace Gravel, 7 m Lambeth Clay, 6 m Lambeth Sand, Thanet Sand.	Base-grouted auger-bored pile, 1.2 m diameter, sleeved over its upper length with its shaft embedded in 4 m Lambeth Sand (green silty clayey sand), 1.3 m Upnor Formation (greenish grey fine silty sand with occasional flint gravel and shell fragments), 1 m Thanet Sand.	Founders Court, Canary Wharf, London. Effective stresses in the Thanet Sand were varied by injecting water around the pile toe. Pile instrumentation indicated a shaft load of 5000 kN under original effective stress conditions, corresponding to an average shaft resistance, $f_s = 210$ kPa or $K = 1.0$ if $f_s = \sigma_v' \, K \tan \varphi'$ and $\varphi' = 33°$.

Table A3. *Summary of key references on pile behaviour in the Lambeth Group (continued)*

Reference	Pile types	Key conclusions
Yeats, J A and O'Riordan, N J (1989). The design and construction of large diameter base grouted piles in the Thanet Sand at Blackwall Yard, London. *Proc 3rd int conf piling and deep foundations, London*, vol 1, pp 455–461.	Base-grouted bored cast *in situ* pile, 1.2 m diameter, 38 m long. 31 m-long sleeve with the unsleeved section penetrating 4.3 m of clayey Lambeth Sand and 2.7 m of Thanet Sand. Instrumented.	Drilled under bentonite. Average shaft friction in the clayey Lambeth Sand and Thanet Sand of $f_s = 185$ kPa. If shaft friction is expressed as $f_s = \sigma_v'K \tan \varphi'$ and $\varphi' = 35°$ this is equivalent to $K = 0.64$.
Gaba, A R (1989). Instrumented driven steel tube piles at Canary Wharf, London. *Proc 3rd int conf piling and deep foundations, London*, vol 1, pp 337–346. Stratigraphy: 2 m of Terrace Gravel, 8 m of stiff Lambeth Clay and 5 m of dense Lambeth Sand, ie piles were mainly embedded in Lambeth Group deposits.	Three instrumented driven open-ended steel tubular trial piles, 1022 mm, 1254 mm and 1524 mm diameter approximately 25 m long and penetrating the Thanet Sand by 0.7–1.6 m.	Pile-driving trials were conducted with three hydraulic hammers. The paper gives examples of driving blowcounts and conclusions. Internal soil plugs were partially cored out and replaced with concrete for pile durability. The piles were tested through axial static and dynamic load tests. Load-displacement curves from static tests showed a distinct change between shaft load and base load. Pile T1 (1022 mm diameter) with the smallest penetration into the Thanet Sand indicated a shaft load of 8600 kN, or an average shaft friction of $f_s = 176$ kPa. Lateral pile load tests and inclinometer readings were used to deduce the lateral soil resistance. This pile type proved an effective foundation solution for the buildings constructed over water at Canary Wharf.
Solera, S A (1998). Continuous flight auger piles in the Woolwich and Reading Beds in the Isle of Dogs, London. *Proc 7th int conf piling and deep foundations, Vienna DF1* Paper 1.9. Stratigraphy: 7 m fill and alluvium, 6 m Terrace Gravel, 1 to 3 m Lambeth Clay, a band up to 1 m thick of coarse sand to cobble-sized nodules of calcareous limestone (SPT $N > 160$), 5 m Lambeth Sand, Thanet Sand.	CFA piles, 600 mm diameter, 16 m long, passing predominantly through fill, alluvium, Terrace Gravel and a small thickness of Lambeth Clay, founded on the limestone band in Lambeth Group with working load of 2000 kN.	South Quay Plaza Phase 2. Static load tests on preliminary and contract piles showed settlements at working load between 5 mm and 11 mm with approximately 50 per cent of working load estimated to be carried in end bearing. Maximum loads reaching 4000 kN were applied with pile settlements of 30 mm. A tension load test indicated a shaft capacity of about 1100 kN, equivalent to an average $f_s = 36$ kPa, after a pile head displacement of about 18 mm. Assuming the same shaft capacity in compression indicates a maximum base resistance of 11.7 MPa or $\underline{N}_q = 62$ on the limestone band. A few piles did not encounter the limestone band and were drilled an extra 1 m deeper and founded in the underlying very dense Lambeth Sand. Load tests showed broadly similar but slightly larger settlements at working load and suggested lower ultimate loads of around 3000 kN. Assuming identical shaft capacities implies base resistances of the order of 7 MPa and $N_q = 34$ approximately. One pile founded on limestone displayed a softer loading response as a result of poorer construction quality with a very rapid rate of auger extraction.

Table A3.4   *Summary of key references on pile behaviour in the Lambeth Group (continued)*

Reference	Pile types	Key conclusions
Chapman, T J P, Connolly, M L, Nicholson, D P, Raison, C A and Yeow, H C (1999). Advances in understanding of base grouted pile performance in very dense sand. In: *Proc symp tunnel construction and piling 99, London, Sep* Stratigraphy: piling platform at -5 m OD, 1 m made ground, 2.8 m Terrace Gravel, 3.9 m Lambeth Clay (stiff grey silty clay), 6.5 m Lambeth Sand, 15 m Thanet Sand, Chalk.	Base-grouted auger-bored pile. 0.9 m diameter, 18.5 m long, founded 5 m into Thanet Sand. Instrumented.	Hongkong and Shanghai Bank Tower, Canary Wharf, London. A trial pile was bored under bentonite. Dewatering was conducted in the Chalk to facilitate construction but bentonite was used to ensure stability. A static load test was conducted in compression. At the time of the load test the piezometric level of the lower aquifer in Lambeth and Thanet Sands was at -9 m OD. Interpretation of the instrumentation indicated unit shaft friction in the Lambeth Clay f_s = 84 kPa corresponding to α = 0.8 with c_u = 100 kPa. In the Lambeth Sand f_s = 105 kPa or K = 1.05 with $f_s = \sigma_v'K \tan \varphi'$ with φ' = 33°.

s/o me
5644(404

CIRIA C583

London 2004

Books are to be returned on or before
the last date below.

E
L

LIBREX —

D

R

D

D
62#. 1509'421
H16

CIRIA *sharing knowledge ■ building best practice*

Classic House, 174–180 Old Street, London EC1V 9BP
TEL +44 (0)20 7549 3300 FAX +44 (0)20 7253 0523
EMAIL enquiries@ciria.org
WEBSITE www.ciria.org

Engineering in the Lambeth Group

Hight, D W; Ellison, R A; Page, D P

CIRIA

CIRIA C583   © CIRIA 2004   RP576   ISBN 0-86017-583-9

British Library Cataloguing in Publication Data

A catalogue record is available for this book from the British Library.

Keywords		
Ground engineering, ground investigation and characterisation, soil-structure interaction		
Reader interest	**Classification**	
Geotechnical engineers, engineering geologists, civil and structural engineers, tunnelling engineers, highway engineers, construction professionals	AVAILABILITY	Unrestricted
	CONTENT	Review of available guidance
	STATUS	Committee-guided
	USER	Geologists, engineering geologists, civil engineers, and drilling and tunnelling contractors